Feasting and Fasting

Paulette Maisner began to realize in her teens that she had a severe eating problem. She tried many remedies, both orthodox and unorthodox, all of which were either of very little help or gave her only temporary relief. In the end she found her own way of solving the problem, and began counselling other sufferers whom she had met as a result of her research. This led in 1981 to the founding of The Maisner Centre for Eating Disorders, 41 Preston Street, Brighton, East Sussex, where people come from all over the world for help.

Jenny Pulling is a journalist who has worked as a feature writer on *Woman's Own* and has contributed articles to national magazines and newspapers both in Britain and abroad. She has also written on medical and general health subjects for specialist magazines. For a while she lived in Italy and worked as a freelance travel writer. Jenny Pulling has devised and presented several radio programmes for BBC Radio Brighton.

Paulette Maisner
and Jenny Pulling

Feasting and Fasting

How to stop yourself
eating compulsively

Fontana Paperbacks

First published in Great Britain by Fontana Paperbacks 1985

Copyright © Paulette Maisner and Jenny Pulling 1985

Set in Linotron Plantin
Made and printed in Great Britain by
William Collins Sons & Co. Ltd, Glasgow

To all the men and women who have attended The Maisner Centre over the past few years and to our agents Frances Kelly and Juliet Burton.

Contents

Acknowledgements

The authors acknowledge with grateful thanks the help and advice they were given by Mrs T. R. Varma, FRCS, FRCOG, PhD, consultant obstetrician and gynaecologist of St George's Hospital; Aileen Chase, Int.BSc, FETC; Martin L. Budd, ND, DO, Lic.Ac; Dr Peter Dally; and also thank Dr Peter Hudson for permission to quote passages from his book *Why Die Young?*

Preface

This book is addressed to you, the compulsive eater. It's also addressed to your friends, to help them understand your problem. The book stems from our own experience of compulsive eating. We want to offer you hope, not condemnation. There is a way out of a condition which can seem to the sufferer endless and inescapable.

This book will not ask you to pull yourself together nor insist that your eating disorder is 'all in the mind'. But we will ask you to believe that you can, if you truly wish it, come to accept food as a normal part of living, regain your self-confidence and achieve control of your self and your life. It won't be easy. There is no miracle cure and we would never pretend that there was. But we believe you can come to understand that 'devil inside you', recognize it for what it is and learn to cope with it. We want to answer that sad, despairing and, unfortunately, familiar question: 'Why can't I stop eating?'

The difficulty with compulsive eating and bulimia is that they cause such guilt that you feel reluctant about coming out and talking about them. Probably they have stayed a secret for so long that you have become used to feeling depressed, hopeless and repelled by yourself. These feelings have swamped the real you, isolating you from the rest of the world. You have come to take it for granted that personal relationships turn sour, that you really have no right to expect a friend, relative or lover to understand your anti-social behaviour because you have to have the food you crave. You know that forcing yourself to be sick, if that is the form your compulsion takes, has some very unpleasant effects on your health and appearance. But the vicious circle, created by stress/lack of control over food/guilt/stress/more food cravings, now seems completely inescapable. You may find that the compulsion is strongest at night and that the guilt at having devoured your family's lunch for tomorrow makes you feel even worse. There are literally thousands of 'secret eaters' and all of them despair of receiving sympathy and understanding. They may be slim and apparently carefree like Hilary whose versatility impresses her friends but who, privately, is unable to communicate or concentrate on any of her goals because of her overriding need to eat. Or they may be like Sarah who is forever exhausted and full of aches and pains, behaves like a vixen, alienates her husband and loses her friends because she can never make any plans for tomorrow. Tomorrow, she knows, will be yet another battle against food. There are also male compulsive eaters like Tom who, after an unsuccessful attempt at suicide, remained tongue-tied when asked why he had behaved this way. He would admit to anything rather than confess to the humiliating truth.

Another difficulty with eating disorders is to get across that anyone, at any time in their life, may embark on the destructive road, often with little warning. The individual who munches through packets of biscuits or crisps in front of the television set has, without realizing it, become out of control, albeit temporarily. This kind of minor compulsive eating can develop into a major problem when life becomes too stressful. Sometimes it is the result of too much hard work over too long a period, and sometimes of boredom, loneliness and frustration. Or it can be caused by the desire for achievement or power.

What we all have to do is to discover our limits and what causes stress in our lives. Compulsive eaters may be extra-sensitive to stress and must be extra-vigilant. Rediscovering a personal balance takes time and patience. But it can be done.

This book, then, is for *them*, for those people for whom

food is an enjoyable experience, the friends and relatives of compulsive eaters among them, in the hope that it will shed some light on the subject so that they may understand the problem and feel less helpless if called upon to cope. It is also for *us*, because the authors identify with everyone who has an eating disorder, having 'been there' themselves.

We should like to add that the names of people whose case histories we describe have been changed.

Finally, we have used feminine pronouns more in the book but should like to emphasize that although it is mainly women who suffer from eating disorders, men are also vulnerable.

Yours compulsively,
Paulette Maisner and Jenny Pulling

1 Paulette and Her Story

They say life begins at forty but for Paulette Maisner the doctor's pronouncement spelt nothing but gloom and doom. 'You've been fat for forty years,' he told her, 'and you will be fat for the rest of your life.' Ever since she could remember, Paulette had suffered from an obsession with food, and sustained an almost life-long battle against obesity, resorting to desperate measures that more than once had landed her in hospital. Like the thousands of other compulsive eaters whose lives have been ruined by their problem but, because of the secrecy that surrounds it, have never become a statistic, she had made the rounds of therapies, searching for an answer. Like them, a part of her isolation had been her shame in admitting the full extent of her bingeing habit and of her constant preoccupation with food, fearful of the disgust she would read in people's faces.

And, as in the case of many doctors who just do not have time for the necessarily long counselling sessions, the cause of her disorder eluded those whom she had consulted. All they had had to offer was something to control the symptoms – tranquillizers, sleeping pills, slimming tablets.

If the reason for her uncontrollable eating was a mystery to Paulette, it presented her doctors with the dilemma of being unable to attach a neat label to this unfamiliar disorder: was it a physical or mental illness? What had caused it and why? They felt unable to help her escape from the cage. They gave her up as a bad job and she was on the point of resigning herself to becoming a medical dropout.

There was a moment, however, in one doctor's consulting room six years ago that marked a turning point. He said there was nothing she could do. Paulette was determined that she would prove him wrong. Since then she has shed several stones and become a controlled eater. She is living a life she had never dreamed would be possible for her, never since those days when, as a sad, fat little girl, she was forever eating.

Teased unmercifully at school, her only popularity was at meal times. Everyone wanted to sit next to her so that she would gobble up the hated stodge. One of her earliest memories is of sitting on the stairs begging not to be forced to go out and 'play with the other children', knowing that they would point at her and laugh. She recalls, too, her exquisitely tiny grandmother weeping over this painfully shy, fat child, while Paulette stared at Granny's 3½-sized shoes and told herself that if she was an ugly duckling, she would never become a swan.

With hindsight, she sees that one of the roots of her problem was being a war baby. It was the early 1940s and she was terrified of the bombs. Her beloved father was away in the army while her mother showed a very obvious preference for Paulette's younger brother. Mrs Maisner, young, helpless and in a strange environment, frankly could not cope. Her mood swung from criticism of her fat daughter to offering food as a reward when the child was good.

At fourteen, the dumpy teenager was sent away to a Swiss school that represented, literally, a land of milk and honey. All that chocolate! Paulette squandered her pocket-money on sweets, which she gorged in secret, while her slim friends disported themselves on the ski slopes or at a tea dance. Their jokes about her size and clumsiness only made her eat more. Her ambition to be thin became a fixation. Instead, however, the pounds crept on because she could not stop eating.

Returning to England, Paulette launched herself into a series of secretarial jobs, none of which lasted long. How could she face the office, bloated and sweating, after a night of bingeing? In desperation, she tried, but could never succeed, making herself sick. Everything had become an effort. Even dressing in the morning was a daunting chore when she had to heave her bulk around. It was about this time that she discovered slimming tablets and latched onto them, believing this might be her salvation. They seemed to work and she experienced a sense of freedom that only another compulsive eater can understand: she did not want to eat. But this was only a temporary freedom. She soon found they were ineffective when she felt the urge to binge.

Yearning for someone to love her, Paulette made a disastrous marriage when she was just seventeen years old. She accepted the first man who came along and three months later he left her. It was then that she tried to commit suicide. There really seemed little left to live for. She was very young and alone and, worst of all, she could not control her eating. During this first stay in hospital, Paulette had time to reflect. Each day she awoke with a phrase ringing in her head and familiar to every compulsive eater: 'Today I will begin. Tomorrow I shall eat normally.' Tomorrow never came.

She became an adolescent bookworm, reading everything and anything remotely connected with the subject, searching for clues to the 'mystery'. During this period, however, all the theories seemed to apply to other people, never to herself. She was living a see-saw existence, losing weight when she had an attentive boyfriend who took her out and about, and putting it all on again when the relationship broke up. Feeling that her young life was passing her by she started going to parties. She soon discovered that a little alcohol broke down her inhibitions and helped her with relationship problems. She drank more and more. Now she imagined she had begun to enjoy life at last but, in reality, she had swapped food for drink. The alcohol that released her inhibitions where personal relationships were concerned, also broke down her tenuous control over food and she started to eat *and* drink. With the amphetamines, Paulette completed the hat trick.

It is hard for anyone who does not have an eating disorder to understand the utter desperation that characterized her endeavours, a desperation experienced by every compulsive eater who will try anything to escape from that secret cage. Finally, she collapsed at the wheel of her car and found herself back in hospital. The enforced rest sent her to the library shelves once more and she discovered Richard Mackarness's *Eat Fat and Grow Slim*. She became a fervent disciple and followed his regime. She stopped bingeing, it was true, but because she was capable of eating more than most people, she simply overate.

The solution continued to elude her and her search for it developed into a major obsession. She founded a self-help group that left her in despair: everyone sat around, moaning about their problems. She attended workshops where the emphasis was laid on the psychological aspect of the problem and sufferers were regressed to childhood. At least, in the company of fellow compulsive eaters, she learned she was not alone and that this was a very common problem.

At this time, she took a job as a receptionist to a leading hypnotherapist who offered to treat her. He encouraged her to try to recognize other needs within her and to fill the empty spaces of her life with positive action. She began to recognize her reflection in fellow sufferers: their inability to communicate, their lack of identity and, among the women, their difficulty in asserting themselves.

When *Fat is a Feminist Issue* was published, Paulette seized on it eagerly but a meeting with some of the author's followers disappointed her. Women, they emphasized, became fat because they were afraid of the closeness of sexual contact with men. The answer seemed to Paulette too glib, moreover she enjoyed men's company. And it didn't explain the male compulsive eater. And what about the woman to whom she had spoken in a supermarket not twenty-four hours ago? She had been cramming chocolate bars into her mouth, with the tears trickling down her cheeks. That woman had been, if anything, underweight and had allowed her family to use her as a doormat. Her panic weeping was brought on because she had lost control. Any human being, female or male, would panic if they lost control over food, drink, drugs, or their lives.

There are no easy answers. Three years ago, however, some of the pieces fell into place. Paulette discovered a relaxation therapy that worked well with stress-induced problems, such as smoking and nail biting. She bought the franchise of a series of video tapes and discovered that, although they worked well with those who were 'normally' obese because they overate, compulsive eaters continued to binge. It confirmed in her mind that *their* primary problem was not gaining weight but lack of control. She read Abrahams and Pezet's *Body, Mind and Sugar*, and Mackarness's *Not All in the Mind*, and noted the parallels between the symptoms and effects they described and the eating patterns of certain compulsive eaters. She joined a workshop run by a specialist in mental health. The results of her findings have been incorporated in the therapy offered by her Centre where she treats and helps other compulsive eaters.

Paulette has come a long way since those days when, like Hannah Bantry in the old nursery rhyme, she hid

> . . . in the pantry,
> Gnawing at a mutton bone,
> How she gnawed it,
> How she clawed it,
> When she found herself alone.

2 The Life of a Compulsive Eater

Inside the cage

Every compulsive eater must have prayed at some time for a 'free' day, one during which she would eat normally, be at peace with herself, be glad to be alive and look forward to the future. But her life style is simply not like that. There is no freedom. Even when she is not bingeing, she continues to count calories, aware that if she does not lose control today, there is no assurance that it will not happen tomorrow or at the weekend, or even in two hours' time! She feels she is locked in a secret cage where the bars are unyielding and there is no escape. Her way of life alternates between feasting and fasting, an obsessional pattern that is difficult to break. And what makes it even more painful is that she believes the 'cage' is unique, and that she is the one and only sufferer of this crippling disorder.

Katey is an attractive young woman who works as a receptionist for a firm of solicitors. She always looks well-groomed, dresses fashionably and is pleasant to clients, who praise her personality. Although she never talks about her private life, her colleagues imagine she enjoys the busy, social existence of any girl of her age. But Katey has a secret. She rides the frightening merry-go-round of feasting and fasting and cannot jump off. 'I have completely lost touch with a normal eating pattern,' she says. 'I am desperate to lose weight and although I am always going on a diet, the minute things get me down I rush out to buy bars of chocolate, sweets, or cakes – anything I can lay my hands on. I binge horrendously, then suffer from guilt and try to cope with this by compulsively starving myself.' Regrettably, Katey's whole life has revolved around fasting and feasting, feasting and fasting, since she began to eat compulsively some five years ago. Now she feels she is a slave to her compulsion and can hardly remember a time when she ate normally.

Harriet is another prisoner who can go for a long time eating practically nothing. She picks at cottage cheese, fruit, slimmers' biscuits, typical items that the compulsive eater allows herself to have in the house. Eventually she becomes depressed because it seems to her she cannot lose any more weight and so she binges. 'If I have a day of gorging like that, there is no way in which I can control myself. I eat enormous meals as well as all the snacks. My binges occur without any apparent pattern, as do the periods of starvation, and I am powerless to stop.'

Compulsive eaters describe this illogical, terrifying pattern in many ways. For some, it is the sensation of being trapped in the middle of a maze, beset by monsters and blind alleyways. They feel literally threatened by food and eating confuses them. They tend to be obsessed by diets, grasping at any new one that makes its appearance, and yet dieting only makes them 'think food' all the more. Says Harriet: 'I seem to have lost my way. I have no idea when I am hungry and should eat nor when I am full and should stop.'

This abnormal attitude towards food and the act of eating steadily draws the compulsive eater into a different and lonely world. She finds she cannot enjoy ordinary pastimes like carrying on a conversation or reading a book. It is very likely that as she stares at the page the words will become unintelligible. While she is, apparently, talking to someone, her mind will be focused on food, on what she has and has not eaten, what she can and cannot eat and when she will eat or not eat again. She views food almost as a tangible creature lurking forever in the background, ready to pounce. She hates and fears it as if it threatened her very personality. And she is usually sensitive and intelligent enough to recognize how these unnatural attitudes are ruining her life. 'I know I will never get a job because I couldn't concentrate on my work at school for thinking about food,' a school-leaver told us. 'I am terrified of bingeing and getting fat. I just want to be able to eat to live and not live to eat.'

None of us wants to be obese, and most of us wouldn't even care to be plump. But while judicious weight-watching may be a sensible idea, the dietary obsession of compulsive eaters submerges all other activities and thoughts. The compulsive eater becomes dominated by an abnormal body image and extraordinary eating habits. Not many people judge the person to whom they are speaking by whether or not they happen to be half a stone overweight. It is, however, of overriding importance to someone like Philippa. In her late thirties, she is happily married with two teenage children who have no idea of their mother's preoccupation. Food, for Philippa, has long ago ceased to be simply essential and enjoyable. She is a sensible woman and very aware that because of her obsession she has become, as she describes herself, 'a very shallow person'. 'And yet I continue to eat constantly, with my mind on what I can eat next while my body is trying to digest the food from previous snacks and meals.'

This tremendous awareness of food as an enemy to be kept at bay creates panic when the compulsive eater knows that she will be exposed to an eating situation that is outside her normal pattern. Geraldine feels 'a terrible panic when I know I shall be eating out and won't be able to count the calories'. As many sufferers will understand only too well, her conflict is usually 'resolved' by stuffing herself. Contrary to general belief, compulsive eaters are not necessarily overweight. Indeed, we go so far as to say that among the majority of sufferers whom we have seen, their weight is normal or even slightly subnormal. And if this is surprising, when we consider the horrifying amount of food consumed during a feast time, we soon remember that this is usually followed by a starvation period. Probing deeper, it becomes evident that, while compulsive eating and compulsive starving are linked with fatness, thinness and a preoccupation with body size, the victim's life style is considerably more warped by her obsession with the food itself – with eating or not eating it. The deep despair she experiences is more likely to be centred on the hopelessness of ever being able to eat normally without guilt or other obsessional thoughts.

Geraldine thinks about being fat all the time and 'worries herself sick' about it. But there are other reasons for her near panic when she has been on a binge. 'Regardless of weight, I just wish I could get through a day eating normally. I wish I could stop hating my body.' Mary's guilt, according to her, is worn like a stigma. 'I refuse to show my limbs and my arms aren't really fat at all. There is a neighbour in my road who is quite plump yet she wears skimpy, short-sleeved clothes. I feel a very unfemale lump – more than that, I can't imagine anyone desiring somebody who binges and vomits all the time. I always confide in people about my problem when I first meet them. I feel loaded with this tremendous sense of guilt and feel I have to apologize for myself and by confessing I put them off.' Mary is extremely pretty, and a talented young artist. No one would guess that she is a compulsive faster/feaster. If anything, it is her overemphasis on her guilt and obsessional attitudes that frighten off the young men. She seems to emanate a sense of weariness, of being absorbed in her compulsion, to the exclusion of everything else.

The effect of the conflict *is* totally absorbing and exhausting, as every compulsive eater knows. It can drive the sufferer to thoughts of suicide. Rosemary goes to bed, worn out by her fight against eating and her guilt when she succumbs. But, as she pointed out, even if her waking thoughts are guilty ones about the binge she had the night before, her food obsession drives her immediately to the kitchen to start all over again.

Because compulsive eating is so guilt-ridden, a good deal of secrecy accompanies it. The 'cage' is even more confining because it is such a secret one. Behind locked doors, alone in bed, in the toilet, or standing by the refrigerator while the rest of the world sleeps, these are all familiar and furtive situations to anyone who suffers from an eating disorder. Their eating takes place at any time, anywhere, except with other people and at the normal place – the table.

Our compulsive eater will often pretend, when shopping for food, that it is for someone else. She'll buy large quantities and stuff herself stealthily. Slender actress Hayley Mills, looking back on a period of uncontrolled eating, admitted that she used to pretend she was shopping for a children's party so that she could buy a huge number of the rich cream cakes for which she longed.

'Nobody ever sees me eat,' Rosemary told us. 'I've become an expert at lying and eating in secret.' We wonder just how many people exist who do eat uncontrollably. Statistics are hard, almost impossible to come by, yet we suspect that a very significant minority of all women has at some time or another experienced this lack of control and panic.

Christine is another of Britain's secret eaters, a fact that is hard to believe as she appears to be a very carefree young woman. Her parents know about her binges but her work colleagues almost certainly do not. At the office she is known as the girl with unshakeable will-power who bypasses the biscuit tin at coffee time and rejects the slice of cake when someone's birthday is celebrated. This is a common trait and victims of eating disorders seem to derive satisfaction from refusing 'goodies' in public, presenting themselves as people with perfect self-control. Only someone who has experienced bingeing can really understand how painful is the need for a public face and, also, how terrifying is the anticipation of being alone and free to eat. The sad truth is that self-control is exactly what the compulsive eater hasn't got. Like a Jekyll and Hyde character, she fears that the moment that piece of cake or biscuit, chocolate bar or ice cream passes her lips, the mask will slip and the 'other' self will take over and she will begin to eat uncontrollably.

Rosemary knows this by heart. She shakes her head firmly

at the proffered plate and can almost see herself sitting back and watching the others enjoy their cream cakes. But her rigid self-denial is usually made up for that night when she goes home to gorge. Ellen described how she 'faithfully refused delicious cakes' and later made for the nearest bakery to buy ten times as many and then sat in her bedroom 'pigging it'. Jean found that, as the conflict between this phantom control and her yearning to eat developed, her mind was in such a state of confusion she had to make excuses to leave work 'simply in order to eat and eat'!

It is little wonder that this behaviour leads to an increasing sense of isolation. Much of our social life is centred around eating, in people's houses, restaurants and clubs. Offering something to eat or drink is usually taken as a sign of hospitality and friendliness. That primitive signal, 'we are not hostile here', continues today at the business luncheon table, the engagement party or the coffee morning for a new neighbour. While people may have time and understanding for those who are diabetic, for example, and who require special diets, or for those who are vegetarian, they become embarrassed or impatient when a guest will not eat for some mysterious, non-apparent reason.

Few compulsive eaters, when they are in the grip of their problem, will 'allow' themselves to eat in a restaurant. Some of them go to desperate lengths to refuse such invitations. Christine has ruined several potential relationships because of this fear and although her eating is becoming under control, her smoking rate doubles on any such occasion and she has a growing sense of unease, which does not make for a relaxed atmosphere. The chaos brought about by the feast/fast pattern also makes life unpredictable, which means that social activities planned in advance present a problem. Sufferers complain that they have insufficient staying power to complete a course of study or exercise, but the greater fear is that they may have binged the night before and will be incapable, physically and mentally, of attending the next session.

Bingeing results in very unpleasant symptoms, not the least being a distended stomach, which is physically uncomfortable and socially offputting, as Rosemary knows well. She has a wardrobe of expensive clothes her fiancé has bought her but there is always a query hanging over whether she will be able to wear them. Rosemary dreads an invitation to go swimming in summer, or dancing in winter, fearful that when the time comes she may have binged the night before and will have to telephone with last-minute excuses. 'I have taken the line of least resistance,' she says. 'I refuse all invitations and stay in. Of course, it affects Michael's social life as well as wrecking my own.'

The bars of the 'cage' seem to grow more impassable and the compulsive eater helplessly watches her life pass her by. Everything is sacrificed to her strange, compulsive attitudes to food and the act of eating. As the stress and tensions mount, she will turn in desperation to pills: tranquillizers, 'uppers', 'downers' and even more addictive drugs. Sandra, a graduate in social sciences, 'throws down' appetite suppressants as if they were Smarties. Then, restlessly pacing the house at night, she tops up with sleeping tablets in order to calm herself. Food tranquillizes the compulsive eater in much the same way as hash calms the junkie or whisky the alcoholic. There is a period when she enters her private world where nothing matters except gorging food and blotting out everything else. Sometimes, it is almost a regression to the past. As she binges on muesli and rice pudding, Yvonne recalls 'sitting in front of the television and my grandmother plying me with bowls of porridge and condensed milk'. For a time the binge tranquillizes and even drugs the victim but sooner or later she is assailed by guilt. She awakens from her dream world to gaze in horror at the wreckage of her ghastly feast. Then tensions and stress build up, only to explode in another mad eating bout.

This is one reason why conventional diets, which restrict the choice of food to arbitrary items, are useless, even dangerous to the compulsive eater. The victim of an eating disorder who puts herself on yet another fad diet is perpetuating her preoccupation with food and her unnatural attitudes towards eating. As Sandra says: 'All my money goes on food and those stupid drugs, in an attempt to wean myself from eating. And the thought only makes me more depressed, so I binge.' This provides another negative link in the chain. Because she feels sick after last night's eating episode, she will miss her morning lectures and drop behind the other students, become anxious and, of course, eat again.

'It's a vicious circle, a damned vicious circle,' says Rosemary. 'You don't go out, and you don't make any attempt at a social life, then you get miserable and tensed up and binge. I just eat and eat and leave everything all over the place. It is mad, crazy, uncontrolled! And when I see it afterwards it is as if someone else had done it, not me.' She sees her problem personified as a 'big black devil', something she has created that takes her over and makes her do things she would not normally dream of doing. She remembers that at the height of her bingeing she shopped on a Friday evening and when by Saturday morning all the food had gone, she would go to the nearby house of a boyfriend and steal food from his larder.

This sense of being out of control, of being dominated by 'the devil inside me', is a leitmotif in a compulsive eater's description of her chaotic life style. Even the choice of foods, the sweet, sugary, refined carbohydrates that form the basis of almost any binge, appears to be 'dictated' by another part of herself. Irene hates this feeling but is still under its control. She described herself when in the kitchen preparing food for the family as 'waiting in terror for the moment when something clicks and I go berserk, stuffing myself as fast as possible with food I normally would not like'. She is conscious that there are times when 'I feel like two people and the evil always seems to triumph over the good'. Sandra's mother cooks for the family but when her daughter is bingeing, she is left to her own devices. Sandra feels as if all her energy and hope are being sapped by this other, fiendish part of her. 'This week, I may seem to be a reasonably slim and normal-looking person but in a matter of weeks I could be a 12-stone slob hiding away from the world.' The comments scribbled across one food chart sent to us by Lorraine read almost like a dialogue with a doppelganger and summed up the constant battle within the divided self. 'I am anxious because a friend is coming round for coffee. Should I offer her biscuits? Yes. If so, shall I have to have one? And how shall I cope with that? Help!' After the friend has left, she eats madly. 'Why? To spite myself? I really have no idea. I do not want to binge. I must be mad. I can't carry on like this. I won't.'

Anatomy of a binge: when, how and why eating becomes uncontrolled

For the compulsive eater locked in her cage life is non-eventful, almost dreamlike. It reaches a crescendo when she goes on a binge. Always conscious of the split part of her personality that is beyond her control, the enemy lurking in the background, she is forever tense and nervous, fearing that her attempts to fight it will not succeed. Sooner or later, that fragile control snaps, the switch is thrown and she gorges. At these times, she feels possessed, likening herself to an insect – 'a locust going through the kitchen'.

What causes a binge? When are the danger times? Where are the danger places? And how are such grotesque quantities of food consumed? Any attempt to analyse bingeing must take into account that it is such a secret, agonizing event. Hardly anyone else ever witnesses it. Nothing is important at that time except food, and any onlooker who *did* chance on such an eating episode would probably be shocked and incredulous both at the manner of eating and the amount consumed. 'I don't know what I'd do if anybody tried to stop me when I am stuffing myself because I feel violent, almost murderous,' Zoe told us, in an attempt to analyse her bingeing when this alien force coerces her to eat. A compulsive feast has nothing in common with the normal overeating of a delicious meal. It is a travesty of a banquet when food that is not particularly liked is stuffed down and certainly not savoured.

What triggers off a binge is a complex question. Often the victim is unaware of the reasons. Margaret is a young, ex-ballet student who, because of injuries sustained during her training, was forced to give up all ideas of a dancing career. She had begun to binge and diet while at ballet school, a habit precipitated by the desire to be more than ordinarily slim. This practice is surprisingly common among dancers, particularly those involved in classical ballet. Her situation is different now. There is no longer the rigid discipline of the ballet nor its demand for downright skinniness, to the point of emaciation. Yet she continues with her binges and is perplexed about her condition. 'My circumstances have changed but so, it seems, have my reasons for bingeing. I find it very hard to explain, even to myself, what starts it off.' Sometimes it seems to her that it is the very act of eating and, fearing this, she tries to delay her first meal until evening, reasoning that at least it will mean fewer binges. Irene agrees that food can be a powerful trigger. She binges 'nearly always after I have eaten when it seems to trigger off a desire, which is hard to control sometimes. It is brought on by eating food that I shouldn't have!' Her life revolves around preparing family meals, a dangerous situation for compulsive eaters because the foods they 'shouldn't have' are often readily available.

The majority of mothers know there are times when they behave like 'dustbins', nibbling the crusts of the bread left over from sandwich-making, tasting while preparing a trifle or sweet, or finishing off the leftover cake on a toddler's plate. For a person with an eating problem this can trigger off a binge. Linda, used to a career packed with deadlines, finds she has developed the habit of bingeing now that she is at home with, as she puts it, 'nothing special to do'. She binges after the children have gone to school, on extra food after lunch and, again, while making the tea. She feels her value as a person has been undermined and longs for more time to know herself, but keeps any aggressive or resentful feelings firmly in check. It is also this form of stress that affects Claire. She prides herself on her appearance and position, enjoys making a pleasant impression on clients and is filled with resentment when asked to do something 'menial', such as change the flower water, which she considers is not part of her job. Claire would never dream of asserting herself or expressing these feelings as she is unwilling to dent her 'nice' image. Instead, such an incident triggers off a chain reaction. She sits down and coolly calculates how much money she has and then, on her way home, stocks up with as much food as it will buy. In the kitchen, she locks the door and eats it as quickly as possible.

Often, however, there is no apparent trigger, only a blind craving for food, a physical and mental desire to eat and eat that is comparable to any other addiction. It may have been an ordinary, happy day at the office with nothing to account for the evening's binge, or a quiet evening spent watching television with the family. But the craving begins and grows and overwhelms its victim, at which point nothing can interest her other than escaping to lay her hands on large quantities of food. 'I can be out with friends, really enjoying myself,' Harriet told us, 'and yet at the back of my mind is what I am going to eat when I get home.'

Rosemary's binges have occurred on such innocuous occasions. By any standards, she should be happy for she has a loving and understanding fiancé and a job she enjoys. Michael often works late into the evening which means she eats alone. On one particular night, as she finished her meal, she remembered that she had bought some bananas and wholemeal rolls for Michael to take for his packed lunch the following day. She was certainly not hungry and felt quite relaxed, ready to start on the household chores. But the image of those bananas on the kitchen table grew in her mind, swamping all other thoughts until she could feel nothing but 'a physical sensation in my throat, an overriding need to eat them'. At last she could resist it no longer. She rushed into the kitchen, tore at the rolls, squashed the bananas into them and emptied a tin of cream on the top. Once she had yielded and begun to eat, all other plans for the evening were forgotten.

'Food has an addictive effect on me,' she told us. 'I consider I am like a drug addict. I crave food as other people crave cocaine and the cravings, when they occur, are too strong for anyone to stop me. Twice I've been in the middle of a binge when Michael returned and I've had to send him out to buy magazines, anything I could think of so that I could continue to eat.' This panic desire for certain foods is similarly described by many sufferers as a physical sensation . . . the feeling of 'something running up and down my arms and the craving starts and then I literally don't stop eating for weeks'.

It is sometimes most powerful at night when a sufferer will wake up around two or three in the morning with an insatiable longing to eat. She will roam the house in an almost somnambulistic way, devouring the contents of the refrigerator. Some report forcing the locks of cupboards to fulfil their cravings – even, in extremity, eating cat food. The consumption of the food is frantic and hurried with no appreciation of taste. There is much more a sense of getting it over with, as if it were a penance that has to be completed. It seems as if the normally accepted concepts of reward and punishment have become confused, just as other food values have become confused. The compulsive eater tells herself she is bad and had better eat all the things she hates and fears, starving herself tomorrow in order to have respite from the repulsion of having stuffed herself until she cannot stand. 'I stuffed myself with sandwiches and biscuits, followed by fish and chips,' Kay told us. 'I seemed to be feeding another, disconnected part of me that was craving those foods that I don't normally eat. Still feeling ill, I proceeded to have more biscuits before I went to bed.'

Because the food is crammed into the mouth with no thought for such niceties as a knife and fork, and because they are usually convenience foods, tinned or packeted items that need no preparation, the victim of such binges does not always realize exactly what and how much she has eaten. It may be only when she or a member of the household goes to the larder or refrigerator the following day and finds that food is 'missing'. Jean remembers such an occasion when she was staying at her son's house for the weekend and, sneaking down in the middle of the night, consumed the contents of a casserole intended for Sunday lunch. 'How do you explain that one away? I dropped the casserole and told them I had broken it.' Her eating is under control now but there are times when she succumbs and binges although these days she can see more objectively what precipitates a binge and has learned to avoid such occasions, people or certain foods.

Her analysis of a binge underlines once more that old feeling of there being a dialogue between the split parts of the personality and how, more than not, the 'devil' wins.

'I had finished work early and my plan was to go to an aerobics class. But it was raining and my period had started. I told myself: "It's raining, you want to go home. You can go straight to bed and you'll be all right."

'"Don't be silly," my other half said. "If you go home you know you will go on a binge."

'"But it's raining. It won't do you any good. And you can go straight to sleep."

'The devil had won so far and when I arrived home that conversation began again. I told myself: "All right, you're home now, go straight to bed. But before you go to bed you must take some aspirin and have a cup of coffee so you must go into the kitchen to make it." When I went into the kitchen I wanted a biscuit to go with the coffee. Upstairs, I felt like another biscuit and by that time I had got the taste for biscuits so I had a handful. Then it was time to have dinner and after that wait for my husband to come in, so I might as well carry on eating. It wasn't a huge binge by my former standards but I felt angry because I knew I could have avoided it by going to my aerobics class. It is always easier to eat!'

Here is the breakdown of a binge that Imogen had one Saturday evening while the family was out: one packet of Ryvita; eight ounces of cottage cheese; a three-egg omelette; a large portion of chips and a Cornish pasty; a box of Dairylea cheese spread; a large packet of crisps; approximately half a large sliced loaf; and cheddar cheese. After this, when there was no food left, she went to a Chinese takeaway and bought a portion of prawn curry, rice, two pancake rolls and a large portion of chips. She ate the lot. 'It was all vile. I collapsed onto the floor and slept there until three in the morning. Then I dragged myself to bed, my heart pounding. I was perspiring profusely and feeling very ill. My stomach ached so much I nearly screamed.'

Apart from the serious effects such quantities of food have on the overworked digestive organs, the cost of these eating bouts can be, to say the least, intimidating. Laura, a graduate in economics, spent a few weeks analysing her binges and costing them out. A day in her life read like this:

6.30 a.m.	Orange juice and coffee	£0.40
9.00 a.m.	4 packets of biscuits, 250 grams of Frosties, 2 pints of milk, 4 bars of chocolate	£2.40
11.00 a.m.	Coffee	
12.00 a.m.	3 packets of biscuits, 250 grams of Frosties, 2 pints of milk, sweets	£2.40
3.00 p.m.	3 pieces of cake, 3 bowls of corn-flakes, milk, 1 packet of biscuits	£1.60
5.00 p.m.	4 slices of toast	
6.00 p.m.	8 oz of cottage cheese and 2 cups of tea	£0.65
7.00 p.m.	1 large natural yoghourt	£0.45
11.30 p.m.	3 fried eggs, 3 sausage rolls, 2 Cornish pasties, 3 spring rolls, 1½ pints of milk	£2.80

It brought the total to well over £10 for the day, and that was nothing like one of Laura's 'bad' days.

There is a vast difference between the obese woman who loves to eat and the compulsive eater who hates food, is afraid of what it will do to her and uses her fasting periods as times of reassurance. She is not gluttonous. Her binges are an attempt to satisfy, albeit chaotically, other needs she senses but cannot define. She is bored and unfulfilled, like Anne, who does not know the difference between hunger and satiety. There is no sense of appetite for the food she stuffs into her mouth. She is merely conscious of bingeing for 'comfort and reassurance'. 'I feel like a pig,' she told us. 'I stuff myself with food, which disgusts me, but I can't stop repeating it over and over again. Then I try to starve it all off again, which I know is wrong.'

The 'ordinarily' gluttonous person is perfectly aware of what she is eating and that she is probably eating too much, but if she feels guilty, the guilt passes because her appetite prevents her from doing much about it. If you compare the eating patterns of a compulsive eater and a normally obese person they are very different. Except when they are bingeing, compulsive eaters deprive themselves. They will go through the day on a boiled egg, coffee, tea and a 'slimming' bar and then embark on a binge that lasts the whole evening. Our obese lady knows she is a pig, regrets it and makes half-hearted attempts to go on a diet but because she never has enough will-power to cut down on the foods she enjoys, she cannot lose weight. On a typical day, she will have lots of toast and marmalade for breakfast and then will pop out for coffee with friends when she will help herself liberally to the biscuit tin as it is handed around. Lunch will include chips because she likes them, a creamy sweet because she fancies it and so to tea and a calorie-laden dinner. This does not take into account the in-between snacks that she cannot resist, nor the fact that she will polish off any leftovers. Such people adore cooking and eating. A present of a box of chocolates would merely give them a momentary pang of guilt. The experience of the compulsive eater is quite different. There is a painting entitled, simply, *The Scream* by Munch. It portrays a woman with her mouth dragged open in a soundless cry which seems to embody fear, desperation, isolation, alienation . . . pain! It is a picture with which many compulsive eaters would identify. It echoes Mary's description of her condition when she is bingeing. She often buys food and eats it as she walks along the street. 'I feel when I'm bingeing, I'm screaming. It is a shout for help. I feel desperate and angry. I go from shop to shop, eating all the time, angry with the people who sell me the food and angry with the people walking in the street. I'm blaming them. I feel helpless because I am doing it and no one knows. Am I the only grotesque animal in existence who cannot help stuffing myself until I am sick?'

Them and us: the division between controlled and chaotic eating patterns

This conviction that they are not 'normal' is strong in many compulsive eaters. Most of us have times, or find ourselves in situations, when we feel we are not behaving as the majority of the human race behaves, but for the victim of an eating disorder, this belief is continuous. She feels alienated, longing to be free from that demon inside her, which appears to have marked her out from the rest of humanity. Why me? she asks herself. Why should I be dogged by this obsession, making me lose all self-respect until I think I am unlovable, unacceptable and not worth a damn? Time and again, in their attempt to express this feeling, compulsive eaters turn to the concept of *them* and *us*.

Is there any truth in the idea that there is a dividing line between those people whose attitudes towards food are rational, and a second group where that is simply not the case? Take, for example, a family of four children, all raised in exactly the same way, given the same amount of attention and opportunity and each fed an identical diet. What causes three of them to have no problems in their pattern of eating while the fourth becomes a compulsive eater? Why does one child, upset by something at school, go off food, while another turns to food for solace? And what should we make of the woman who dreads the weeks her husband is away on a working trip because she knows she will binge continuously, whereas others in a similar situation would lose their appetite?

Eating, for compulsive eaters, has become an issue confused with emotion. As Sandra told us: 'I feel I am in my own private hell and I don't know how much longer I can go on. I am ugly, fat and different. Other people go off their food when they feel anxious, I put on weight. When I am depressed all I want to do is to rush home, take the telephone off the hook and demolish the contents of the kitchen.' Irene, surrounded by an affectionate family, always, it seems, in the hub of things, senses 'a feeling of isolation, alienation even, when I am in a group of people, which is hard to live with'. And turning to Claire once more: 'I react badly to stress, particularly stress at work. Unlike other people, if I am upset my appetite runs amok and dominates me. I can think of nothing else except eating.'

Sensing this difference, compulsive eaters yearn to be like *them*, those much envied people with no eating problems who can have one piece of apple pie, one small cake, or a normal portion of trifle without its launching them onto a private binge. *They* can have a snack when they feel like it or an ice cream. A compulsive eater would feel terribly guilty if she succumbed and would then think about food for hours and either plan to fast or binge as a consequence.

Because of their feelings of guilt and their use of food as an unsatisfactory solution to their emotional needs, they begin to see themselves no longer as worthwhile as *them*. They have, they believe, forfeited the right to join in an active, positive life and must stay on the sidelines as spectators. They are forever postponing living until some magic day when they will become like *them*. And even if life goes well for a short time, their reactions are by now so habitual that they may well continue to behave like those who are damned.

Mary remembers a good day when she graduated from art college and was highly praised during the exhibition of some of her paintings. She felt at peace with the world while she was with other people, even ate and drank normally with them. But when she arrived home, she suddenly became tense and anxious and told herself that she could not cope with happiness in the way that other people could. 'I thought, "So what, so you're happy and you're already counting calories. You feel bored and depressed." I could feel the need to eat increasing until I binged. I know I have a lot going for me. I have my art and my friends. I wish I could be content with normal everyday things like *them*. But when you're used to this pattern of behaviour any strong emotion disturbs the balance and it is much easier, anyway, to stick to your old habits.' She dislikes her behaviour but, deep down, is unwilling to change and feels unable to summon up enough energy to do so. This despair of ever being normal creates further alienation.

Rosemary works with several young women of her age but feels there is some unnamed reason why she cannot bring herself to approach them and join in their conversation. She tries to wear a mask of capability and self-assurance but there is the abiding sense of being unable to be sociable until she can come to terms with her problem.

Ironically, it is very unlikely that anyone has this 'perfect', controlled eating plan that compulsive eaters imagine *they* have. Most people have days when life goes well and other days when they feel annoyance, self-disgust, depression or a sense of inferiority. Most people have days when they overeat, or snack on junk foods. They are certainly not perfect. Mary, wishing she could live with one of these disciplined and mythical people so that her eating habits might be monitored, would discover that 'normal' attitudes to food and eating are not always disciplined attitudes. Yet Mary continues to keep herself isolated, waiting for the day when she will become 'normal'. She lays the blame for her problem on anyone and anything, rather than accept herself as she is – not very different from the rest of the human race. Her true foe is not food but lies elsewhere.

'I feel tired and worn out, working all the year just to keep myself in food, tablets and cigarettes,' says Sandra. 'I look at other girls shopping for clothes and buying themselves treats. It would be wonderful to be like *them* and not have to worry incessantly about one's food intake and weight.' A life spent in a state of despair at the large amounts of food consumed, or of elation at the lack of food eaten on a particular day, or when emotion makes you gobble at random, using food as an alcoholic uses whisky to blur the world, seems like madness. And it is true that some compulsive eaters believe they are going insane. Their isolation and their belief that no one else can possibly share their unsociable habits, increase their fear. Some have no label for their condition. Knowing only that they have an insatiable hunger that they cannot rationalize or control, they think they must be disgustingly 'greedy'! Often, lack of understanding from the people around them adds to this idea of insanity and gluttony. Sufferers feel they should 'pull themselves together'. Yet the compulsive eater is often a sensitive, intelligent person whose life has become paralysed by her obsession.

Sufferers become convinced that, even if *they* do not see them eat, *they* 'know'. A binge leaves them feeling hung over, every bit as much as if they had had a night out on the tiles. They are bloated. Their faces are puffy and their eyes half closed. They are sometimes aware that the colossal amount of food they eat produces unpleasant body odours and even a small binge will leave them feeling guilty and angry. They certainly do not want to mix with *them* at times like these. One group of compulsive eaters was asked to imagine they had become two of *them* and to have a conversation in which they described the two sufferers to one another. They were deeply critical and disparaging, using adjectives like 'slovenly', 'irritable' or 'anti-social', and clearly felt that their problem was all too apparent. Yet compulsive eaters would be astonished to know how 'invisible' their problem really is. People are usually too concerned with their own affairs to take much notice.

Of course there are physical signs but they tend to be immediately obvious only to the sufferers. Geraldine longs to be free. She wants to go and see the man she loves, and from whom she has not heard for two months. She knows he would be pleased to see her again 'if I looked beautiful'. She *is* beautiful but she will not be for very much longer if she continues to make herself vomit. Her skin has already coarsened, showing tell-tale signs of her excesses, and her eyes are often bloodshot. She is beginning to dislike what she sees in the mirror each morning. Rosemary's intelligence would make her an asset at any social gathering but she refuses 'hundreds of invitations' because she has become hopeless, convinced that everyone knows about her anti-social habits. She feels as if everyone stares when she comes into a room and is helpless to do anything about it.

But if the physical signs identify the compulsive eater, it is probably the mental aftermath that is more alienating – those feelings of guilt, shame, inferiority and self-repulsion. Because she feels she is contemptible, her expectations are probably more limited than *theirs*. She is apologetic about taking up space. She feels that other people's wants and needs are more important and that she should not refuse requests, however unreasonable. She may have problems over the question of identity. Unlike *them*, the group that has somehow earned the 'right' to a carefree life because *they* obey the rules, she feels that, if she asserts herself and says 'no', when 'no' is justified, she will not be a nice person, able to mix with other people. 'I must keep my head up and my mouth shut,' Sandra told us, looking towards what she saw as another doomed year. 'I wish I had the guts to stand up for myself like other people seem to do,' she said. 'It's just that I am not like them. I am always going to do so but never do.' Sandra perpetuates a vicious circle: poor self-image, fear of asserting herself, depression, binge/binge, depression, fear of asserting herself, poor self-image.

In common with many sufferers she has a total inability to commit herself to do anything likely to take her attention away from eating. She can never sustain a series of exercise classes nor keep up with a course of study, if she enrols in the first place. She cannot believe she has the capacity to stop being impulsive, slow down and become absorbed in something unconnected with food. It is not that she is particularly fond of her own company. Alone, she finds it hard to relax with a book and soon begins to feel anxious, bored or restless and turns to eating. Words like 'restlessness', 'boredom', 'depression' and 'inadequacy' crop up frequently in the conversation of sufferers. Since she gave up her ballet training, Margaret has felt bored with life, has lost all her confidence and has come to dislike herself. At the moment she is convinced that it was not only her injuries that caused her to give up her career but also something innately 'different' in her make-up, which prevents her from making a success of life when other people can. 'I have a general lack of interest in wanting to do anything. It is too much trouble. I can think of several things I would like to do but there is always a reason why it's not possible and I end up bingeing,' she told us. Some compulsive eaters find that this apathy and a kindling of optimism are fluctuating moods. It often seems to depend on their body image at the time and the success with which they have coped with the effects of bingeing and fasting. Some have a 'confident' wardrobe hung with fashionable clothes, for those times when they feel thin and normal, and an 'unconfident' one of dowdy garments when their 'fat' personality is dominant and they feel they do not belong to the human race. Mary wore one pair of unflattering, floppy trousers for several months after she had put on a stone because of her bingeing. When she lost weight and felt confident and feminine, she branched out into modern, attractive clothes, expecting to receive wolf whistles and did so. Madeleine finds this contrast almost frighteningly sharp. There are times when she has crossed the border from *us* to *them* and has been capable of asserting herself. But when the bad times came again, her 'fat' self could not cope with some of the activities undertaken by its slim counterpart. Significantly, one of these activities was to become the group leader of a slimming club.

One of the worst aspects of this *them* and *us* concept is that the victim of an eating disorder is usually aware that life is passing her by while she remains isolated from 'normal' people. She regrets the opportunities lost because of her food obsession but feels powerless to alter the state of affairs. Even when bingeing becomes under control and her self-image improves as the fat diminishes, she fears the onset of anxiety or depression, knowing that the old response to food will return. However dimly, she is forever aware that she will never really become like *them*.

Many women who suffer from compulsive eating feel they have forfeited the chance of finding a husband and having children. They cannot face up to the idea of having their habits observed closely.

Claire told us: 'I won't face up to whether I am really a frigid woman, that is, if a relationship were ever formed, which is hardly likely. I can't imagine anyone putting up with me.' Even if she shrinks into apathy, postpones living and uses food and eating to shield herself from social pressures, most compulsive eaters have a picture of the life they might have if ever they left the ranks of *us* and became one of *them*. There *is* a passport out. Compulsive eating can be controlled but it is a battle all the way, an unrelenting one, and an initial step is to stop trying so hard to be 'normal' and to recognize that normality, as the compulsive eater sees it, does not exist.

Said Lucy: 'I have been out of the "cage". I felt wonderful, worked better and lived better. My social life was good but now I'm back inside again. It seemed inevitable and also a relief to be back in a "safe" environment. I know I could be more like *them*. The answer is in my hands but it is not easy.'

The impossible dream: the quest for perfection

Compulsive eaters expect too much of themselves and of other people. If I didn't have this obsession with food, they tell themselves, I should immediately become more carefree and relaxed and enjoy social events. If only I did not have to worry about food and weight, I should have no other problem. They are convinced they would be enthusiastic, capable and generally a nicer person to know. The energy consumed in the continual preoccupation with food would be released and they could become useful and make the world a better place. This notion of perfecting themselves and their surroundings and of inhabiting an ideal world is a characteristic one. It has certainly become a fixed idea in the minds of too many compulsive eaters. The only obstacle to a happy, fulfilled life, according to their lights, seems to be their inability to control their eating habits. Once this is achieved and their intake of food is perfected, there will be no stopping them. Wishes will be granted and life will become serene and problem-free.

The formula, they believe, is very simple: *happiness* = a slim body (and a skinny one is even better). Does this sound familiar? It is what many fad diets promise, if not overtly. Stick to my regime, deprive yourself of food and you will become slim and successful . . .happy!

Believing that *they* adhere to a perfect eating plan with no slip ups, and convinced that a slender figure can be the result only of unrelenting and strict dieting, our compulsive eater sets herself a programme of rigid dietary control. If she deviates even slightly she feels the same guilt as if she had gone on a massive binge. She slips. She eats. She binges!

We asked a group of people with eating disorders to think

about their everyday lives and to set themselves some goals they should like to achieve. We also asked them what they expected their level of achievement would be. People wrote down such activities as washing up *immediately* after every meal. They discussed carrying out a programme of serious study, at least two hours every day, without fail. One girl said she would catch up on her letter-writing, contacting all those people she had neglected. A fourth set, as her target, to decorate the whole of her house while a fifth said she would attend an aerobics class six times a week. Overall, as we soon realized, these people had very high expectations of themselves. The house decorator might more reasonably have said she would prepare one room. Two aerobic sessions a week would have been a possible goal. It was also apparent that these people were dubious as to whether they could live up to their programme. At the end of a week, we met up again and looked at the graphs we had drawn up and checked how far each had come in achieving her goal. None had got anywhere near it.

As we pursued this exercise, the group came to learn that if they had been more realistic in their goal and less harsh on themselves, setting a level somewhere in the middle, they might easily have accomplished it. This exercise proved useful and gave them an insight into the causes of that rigid fasting which was inevitably followed by feasting. Mary knows this chain reaction well. She 'broods over calories', feeling desperately guilty if she breaks the 'rules' she has created for herself. One extra carrot or half an apple during her deprivation periods and she castigates herself, wondering where she has gone wrong. She writes down every single item she eats and carefully calculates its calorie value, balancing it against the number she feels she is justified to eat in a day. Mary's attitude has become such an obsession that the realization that her 'sums' are wrong, that she has eaten 150 calories more than her allowance, sends her into a frenzy. Her diary notes an entire evening spent regretting the few fruit gums she ate. The truth is that she ate them because she was hungry. The eating plan she has inflicted on herself is at starvation level. If she continues in this way, her body's metabolic pattern will go increasingly haywire and Mary will binge. Her body is craving the substances it is not receiving and she is losing control. If Mary would let herself eat a little more, which she could well afford to do, she would not put on weight and she would find that much needed balance.

Let us take another case, that of Susan who started to lose weight. She went from 12 stone to 10 stone. But the results she had hoped for did not materialize. Her love life and work life did not suddenly improve. She then set herself to diet anew. If she could succeed in lowering her weight from 10 stone to 9 stone, she reasoned, everything would be fine. At 9 stone again, nothing changed. Susan's weight goal was now fanatically set at 8 stone. That was when she began to put her fingers down her throat in an attempt to make herself vomit; that was when the stress built up, the gnawing tension and anxiety, and the nasty battle began between eating to live and living to eat. A narrowing of interests until food becomes the overriding focus of attention happens to anyone who is starving. That is what Susan is doing to herself now. She has set an unreasonable goal, expecting her body to accept, indefinitely, an unbalanced, starvation-level diet. She dwells on food as deprived Ben Gunn, stranded on a desert island, dreamed of toasted cheese. She binges. She fasts. Her stressful, diet-haunted personality is not designed to make her popular and the happiness that she seeks becomes increasingly elusive.

Compulsive eaters are even less able to tolerate semi-starvation than other people. They become tense, irritable and find fault with other people, which, as they know only too well, is a sound basis for bingeing.

Mary, the calorie-counting artist, has lots of talent as her graduation exhibition proved. But now that she has left college and the approval of her tutors and is confronted by a cold, cruel world, she is afraid to start looking for work. Her extremely high expectations of herself and how well she ought to succeed paralyse her. 'I want things to go very well,' she told us. 'I want to do so many things but it is hard to get myself to do them because I keep worrying I shan't succeed, instead of just getting on with it. There is a part of me that believes in my work very strongly and I know if I put my mind to it and try hard, I can do anything. I ought to go round with my portfolio but my big fear is that if people criticize my work they will be criticizing me. If people don't like it, then I am wrong in my judgement. I'm living in cloud cuckoo land.' It brings her to the brink of yet another vicious circle. If, as it seems to Mary, she has no control over her destiny and is doomed to failure before she begins then the easiest thing in the world is to turn to her body image. This she *can* do something about. She *can* limit her food. She *can* count calories and keep her eating under strict control. Her concern with being found wanting or not living up to expectations is turned inwards on herself.

Compulsive eaters can also have unrealistically high expectations of *them* – particularly when *they* are husbands or boyfriends. Rosemary is aware that control over eating lies in her own hands but still blames Michael for not arriving home when he is expected, thus precipitating a binge. 'He knows what happens. He knows I have an eating problem,' she exploded. Michael would like her to take the strain off him and realize that he, too, is sometimes in quiet despair about life. Try as he may, he cannot measure up to her expectations of him as a 'normal' person. If he is late, she greets his apologies with the accusation that he has caused her to empty the refrigerator. If, on the other hand, he offers understanding, she is irritated because she feels she is being humoured and she resents that, too. As people like Rosemary get better, their expectations of the world and of themselves become less rigid. Their growing control over their lives enables them to tolerate the human faults of others. But until there is that improvement, disappointed expectations can lead to bitterness.

When Margaret 'came out' and confided her secret to her

family, telling them the extent of her eating disorder, she had overestimated their love and understanding. She felt that the family were there to support and help her. Now she feels even more isolated and disillusioned. Of course she has a right to expect support but not to the extent she continues to demand. Her family are concerned about her problem but they have, naturally, continued to live their own lives. There are times when they are caught up with their own fears and anxieties but, according to Margaret, they have let her down. Sometimes, she can admit that they have tried to be helpful and she realizes that she expects too much. But sometimes, and according to her mood, she is an impossible perfectionist, critical of herself and of them. Margaret looks like an angel with her pale porcelain skin, baby-blue eyes and blonde hair. But this ethereal appearance hides a demanding young woman who cries out for attention, love and care and continues to use her eating disorder to draw attention to herself.

Rosemary is beginning to accept that people are not as perfect as she would like them to be. She knows the basics of good nutrition and although she sometimes fails to adhere to them and becomes depressed, she is slowly learning to reason with herself more and remember that there is always tomorrow and time to try again. The pressure is lifting and she finds she can accept imperfections in other people. The world will not grind to a halt if a friend arrives half an hour late.

Degrees of chaos: bulimia and anorexia

The daily eating pattern of a compulsive eater is chaotic. Meal times are meaningless. 'Breakfast', 'lunch' and 'dinner' might almost be a foreign language. For a compulsive eater breakfast could mean anything from half a cup of coffee to a binge that included biscuits, peanut butter, chocolate and rice pudding. She is too scared to accept invitations to lunch or dinner because she knows she will either refuse all food and drink, then binge when she arrives home, or make a pig of herself and spend half the evening in the lavatory, throwing up.

Life for most 'normal' people, those in the *them* category, is punctuated by meals taken at more or less regular intervals. They might snack in between or occasionally skip a meal, but there is usually some time during the course of a day when they sit at table with knife and fork to eat. Yet meal times for the compulsive eater are overshadowed by the fear of becoming out of control.

Katherine is consumed with guilt because she will sometimes eat an ounce or two of fudge or some ice cream which she had no conscious intention of eating. She is one of those whom we call 'part-time' compulsive eaters, like the woman who nips out to buy a bag of crisps when no one is about because so long as it is secret, it does not 'count'. The crisps may be a reward for being 'good' and completing a task or compensation for a day that went badly. Although their consumption is vastly different, there is probably little to choose between the guilty reaction of Katherine and that of Fiona whose blow-by-blow account of a chaotic twelve-hour binge startled even us. Her notebook describing how she 'set herself up' for the binge with a Scotch and lemonade reads all the more horrifically because of her awareness of what she was doing – this sense of watching another, disorganized part of her personality take over.

As she munched and crunched her way through the crisps and potatoes, the jumbo sausages, packets of biscuits, packets of 'snacks', the mince-pies, fruit-sundae pies and cans of cream, she also described the confused state of her room as having been 'hit by a hurricane', adding that this upset her because she 'normally' liked things to be kept in order. That binge ended at six in the evening. An hour later, Fiona decided it was time for 'dinner' and she started to prepare it: mince with garlic and red wine and mounds of spaghetti. Meanwhile, she had vomited in order to rid herself of the food she had already eaten, and so began to eat again, nibbling on more crisps while she prepared the food and opening up another can of cream. She 'crashed around' the kitchen, shouting at the landlady and spilling food.

By now she had a raging, throbbing headache which drove all reasonable thought away. Her control lessened progressively and she continued to comfort herself with a large tin of rice pudding, more biscuits with margarine and two packets of instant custard. This eating chaos is contrasted with the continued loathing of her room. She wrote: 'I want to tidy up everything so that it looks orderly.' Instead, she ate until she felt nauseous, forcing down food until after nine in the evening, and then she vomited. She continued to write up the binges, leaving out letters because of the chaotic state of her mind. Tomorrow, she promised herself, would be a new start and she would eat only at meal times. 'Breakfast' next day was at half past eleven. It was another chaotic 'meal' of peanut butter and golden syrup, crispbread, biscuits, custard, biscuits, biscuits and more biscuits and, finally, ice cream. Fiona vomited and rid herself of all that food, once again.

She suffers from bulimia nervosa, the medical term used to describe the eating disorder that is accompanied by self-induced vomiting or the futile taking of laxatives and diuretics or both. They are all designed to purge the body of the vast quantities of food that have been ingested. Vomiting relieves the dreadful discomfort, the distension and bloated feelings and makes room for the next binge. The Roman vomitarium is still with us in the eighties. Once purpose built, a place where gluttons might empty their stomachs after a feast, only to return to the table, today it is likely to be the lavatory. Here, in a sort of rough justice, the discomfort of vomiting assuages the binger's guilt. Bulimia combines the obsession with food with an exaggerated fear of obesity and the only way the sufferer can relieve such chaotic, confused lines of thought is by trying to vomit the food eaten. This brings a degree of relief. As Hilary put it:

'I have a greater feeling of satiety after vomiting. I only wish I had this feeling of satisfaction after eating a meal.' But the gorge/purge pattern is followed by overwhelming self-disgust and a sense of worthlessness and the only release is to binge again.

Once vomiting is established as a 'way of life', it is a habit that is hard to break. As time goes by it becomes like any addiction, self-perpetuating. The bulimic may feel hungry, guilty, under stress and dehydrated all the time and because of this will eat or drink more, inducing the bloated feeling, more guilt and the need to vomit again. It is a vicious circle that becomes almost impenetrable. Bulimics are aware they are wasting their lives. They know it is counter-productive but breaking that circle is another matter.

Bulimia may be a mild-sounding word but its effects can be very unpleasant, even dangerous. One of its hallmarks is a mouth of rotting teeth caused by the strong acid constantly washing over them. Repeated vomiting can also lead to loss of minerals, such as potassium, gastric disturbances from the loss of stomach secretions and even tearing of the oesophagus. Vocal cords become inflamed and the victim is aware of a puffy appearance; the eyes become bloodshot and, in extreme cases, the heart may be affected because of the severe potassium imbalance or epileptic fits may occur. The serious repercussions of such a practice were evident in the short life of the model Pauline Seaward. She died at the age of twenty-four, following an enormous binge. Ms Seaward had spent six years feasting and fasting. Her last meal included two pounds of raw kidneys, one and a half pounds of raw liver, two raw cauliflowers, three pounds of raw carrots, ten peaches and several pounds of fruit. Her intestines were so badly damaged that she died of gastro-enteritis.

In our experience, bulimia is often associated with some previous involvement in a slimming organization where the sufferer was subjected to the bouquets and brickbats of fellow slimmers.

Brenda already had a weight problem when she met a girl at a party who ran a slimming club. The other seemed to be able to eat without any anxiety about her slender figure. When Brenda, an ex-model, caught her 'in the act' of vomiting, she decided to try this method herself. 'It wasn't easy at first. I tried sticking my fingers down my throat and, after a time, I was able to vomit every time I had eaten something. It seemed, at the time, I had found the answer to my problem. I began to lose weight but the vomiting became addictive until I made myself sick even though I'd practically starved myself. I reached my goal weight and began to eat again. Then I put on the pounds and started to vomit. I should like to say to any girl who thinks this is the solution to her weight problem that the moment you stick your fingers down your throat you have set yourself on the road to a bloated, "fat" appearance. It is to do with the potassium loss which upsets the water balance, thus encouraging water retention. I have suffered from bulimia for the past five years and it is a living hell. I don't know why I do it any longer, but I cannot stop.'

Some sufferers of bulimia derive almost a sexual satisfaction from their vomiting as it gives immediate relief from the tensions built up during the binge, from the discomfort of the fullness and from the fear of obesity. This naturally encourages the desire to repeat the procedure. Some people cannot make themselves vomit and may resort to taking extremely large doses of laxatives to make certain the food is not absorbed. Margaret vomits and purges. At the time she was told to lose some weight after an audition for the Ballet Rambert, she saw a programme on eating disorders and this gave her the idea of vomiting. She has since used the method 'successfully' and has also taken up to fifty laxative tablets at a time in a panic attempt to keep her weight down. Bulimia is not a new phenomenon, although it has come to the fore fairly recently. The name is composed of 'bous', the Greek word for ox, meaning something extraordinarily large, and 'limos', meaning a ravenous hunger. It is to be found in Liddell and Scott, citing a reference in Aristotle. Interestingly, the Oxford English Dictionary instances it in English in 1389 and defines it as 'a morbid hunger, chiefly occurring in idiots and maniacs . . . the so-called canine hunger'.

During the past decade or so, doctors have noted that bulimia appears to be contagious among young women living at close quarters, as in a training college or school, particularly those associated with modelling or ballet. They 'catch' the practice from one another until there may well be a whole dormitory of girls, vomiting on a regular basis to rid themselves of unwanted food. With an ever-increasing emphasis placed on extreme slimness as a desirable goal, doctors fear its increase. At the moment, however, they are not entirely convinced of the association between bulimia and anorexia nervosa. Our experience with compulsive eaters also suggests that, although almost half of those we see have at some time in their lives suffered from anorexia nervosa, bulimia and anorexia are different in many respects. One significant difference is in the stop/go eating signals. Anorexics have successfully held theirs at 'stop' for the most part. Those who eat compulsively have one set of signals that operates correctly in the presence of other people but goes wild when they are alone. Another difference is in appearance. While sufferers of both disorders have a powerful desire to keep their weight below a self-imposed threshold, bulimics are generally heavier, more sexually active and more likely to menstruate. Loss of periods is an essential symptom of anorexia nervosa. The disorder begins with pubescence among young girls and, less frequently, boys, and is marked by an unrelenting desire to lose weight by refusing to eat. But slimming itself does not amount to anorexia nervosa, nor is it simply a question of having gone too far with food deprivation. A more telling hallmark is the stolid denial of hunger and the wish to continue to lose weight even when it is obvious to everyone else but themselves that they are skinny, to the point of emaciation.

Many bulimia sufferers complain of feeling 'too tired' while the anorexic is notable for her unbounding energy, amazing those around her by continuing strenuous exercises when she looks far too frail to carry them out. One of the writers recalls the ritualistic programme of exercise and activities she felt compelled to carry out every day during a period when her weight was under 6 stone. Intellectually, anorexics may agree with people that their idea of being too fat is exaggerated but, emotionally, they continue to deny it. 'It is as if I take a joy in doing something that others can't do. I am maintaining a control, which is beyond *them*, although I am aware of the way in which I am injuring my body,' Rita told us. She described her preoccupation with food and how she enjoyed cooking elaborate dishes for other members of the family. When she watched them eat it reinforced her own dieting achievement.

Protest hunger strikes are powerful persuaders as the wasted limbs and hollow cheeks have such an agonizing effect on those towards whom the fast is directed. Anorexia nervosa has much in common with this. We see it not so much as a loss of appetite but as a form of fasting. The steady loss of weight is the epitomy of self-control, producing a sense of achievement and elation, and is even used as a form of blackmail. The girl, who is protesting or crying out for help by the use of this fasting habit, can cause her relatives feelings of intense guilt and anxiety. It becomes even more distressing for the whole family because she often does not understand why she is doing it herself, nor can she explain what she wants or what she is protesting about. 'I felt as if my parents expected too much of me. My father's a professor of biology and my mother is pretty and intelligent. I didn't see how I could live up to them,' Rita told us. 'I wanted to please them and I was afraid of failure but we've never discussed such things in our family. The only area of my life over which I seemed to have control was my body. I starved myself.'

Anorexia may begin as a protest or cry for attention but,

as malnutrition gains a hold, the cause and effect become muddled and indistinguishable. The condition that may have a psychological cause results in physical effects. Lack of the correct balance of nutrients upsets the glandular and nervous systems and with the development of food intolerances and the lowering of blood sugar levels, another vicious circle may be set up, which could lead on to compulsive eating. Rita's attitude can be seen as typical of many adolescents in this decade, especially those like her who are attractive and intelligent and of whom so much is expected. By fasting and losing weight, it is possible to regress to a helpless state. Periods cease and sexual feelings disappear. Not eating is a way of protesting against the pressures and gaining attention.

Although, on the surface, anorexia nervosa and compulsive eating seem to have something to do with control or lack of control over eating and too much concern with the body, the crux of both matters lies elsewhere. According to Dr Hilde Bruch, acknowledged as a leading authority on anorexia nervosa and other eating problems, the 'slimmers' disease' is prefigured by disturbances in body image, the failure to recognize nutritional needs and an underlying sense of being unable to change one's life.

While it is, predominantly, adolescent girls who suffer from this problem there are also young men who develop both anorexic and compulsive-eating problems. The physician Richard Morton described the condition during the eighteenth century when he mentioned a boy who had become depressed, refused to eat and consequently was reduced to skin and bone. We have seen several young men who undoubtedly suffer from eating disorders. For example, Stephen telephoned with what seemed like an odd request: 'Monks can fast for a long time. How long can I go without eating?' Questioned, he told us that he had not 'eaten for weeks' and now, at 5 feet 11 inches, he weighed 9 stone. In spite of this, he said he could not lose his 'big calves' of which he was very self-conscious. His was not a protest, he was simply determined to 'lose' his calves even if it meant starving himself to death.

Anorexia nervosa is a condition where needs and feelings are dampened down because to express them results in anxieties. Young men are encouraged to be aggressive and in adolescence are often surrounded by friends or a gang. Adolescent girls are more likely to be persuaded to subdue those feelings.

Whether the problem is bulimia or anorexia nervosa there are factors they have in common: an obsessional view of food, eating habits and weight loss to the extent that it interferes with the sufferer's life; a distorted body image where the sufferer sees herself as being 'fat', although according to normal criteria she is not; and a conviction that life would be happy if she were thin.

But, as previously noted, each disorder has symptoms that are somewhat unique. Sufferers from anorexia nervosa have an intense fear of obesity, even when their weight is well below normal. She may say she feels fat even though she is emaciated and that she likes the way she looks, taking exception to the concern of friends. She diets to the point of fasting and is a compulsive exerciser. While she may eat very little herself she remains preoccupied with food and may collect recipes or cook meals for others. Generally, she is aware that she is hungry but exerts an amazing control to conquer it. Her weight loss is over 25 per cent of her original body weight but her periods may cease before a great deal of weight is lost. Later, there will be signs of malnutrition, such as confusion, feeling cold even at the height of summer, losing hair and, at the same time, growing a fine body hair.

The symptoms of bulimia are different. The victim has a binge/purge pattern of eating. She eats large quantities of food, often of the sweet and starchy varieties, and then vomits to avoid gaining weight, or she purges and uses laxatives, diuretics and enemas, or she fasts. The degree of the binge differs from person to person. For some, an ordinary-sized meal may represent a binge, for others it is a period of gorging. What distinguishes them as bulimics is that they will all vomit or purge. Bulimics feel depressed and guilty after a binge and their lives become dominated by this eating pattern, which interferes with health, a career and relationships. They may reach the point of preferring to eat and purge alone instead of being with companions. While their weight can sometimes fluctuate greatly, the loss is never as great as is the case with anorexics.

While both tend to have low self-esteem, the bulimic is less passive than the anorexic who is likely to be less sexually active. Bulimics may also use alcohol and drugs and many report depression and alcoholism in the family. Obviously both eating disorders can cause many serious, sometimes fatal, physical problems.

Outside the cage, looking in: the helplessness of parents and friends

For the relative or friend, outside the cage and looking in, compulsive eating presents a bewildering and frightening condition, one with which they often feel helpless to cope. A man may be the most loving, sympathetic and understanding in the world, a parent may be the most devoted and giving, but even they, confronted by a wife or daughter who blots out everything except food, must come to the conclusion she does not care about their feelings.

Compulsive eating is a very painful and private affair. Compulsive eaters binge, vomit and swallow numerous purgatives in secret. Their self-repulsion and feelings of being second-class citizens, not worth a damn, and the guilt, deception and shame that breed their chaotic eating patterns, urge them to keep their tracks covered at all costs. They shop furtively for food, pretending it is for someone else, eat at odd places and dare not go out socially for fear they may slip up and reveal their complaint. Sooner or later, however, the people who are nearest and dearest to them, husbands, lovers, mothers, fathers and friends, begin to suspect that something is amiss. That sense of a dual personality, the 'devil inside me', that at times has ascendancy over every compulsive eater, driving her to eat, creates mood changes. They are 'symptoms' that just cannot be ignored.

Picture if you will this domestic scene. It is evening, the meal is over, and the television is switched on. Husband and wife settle down to watch it. During the course of the evening, she munches her way through not one but three packets of biscuits. He never really realized his wife overate but now watches her, amazed. Finally, he blurts out: 'My god! You are a pig!' As time goes by and she continues to binge on biscuits, he becomes increasingly annoyed and questions her why she does it. She stares at him blankly. She does not know! But now that he has made her see herself as strange and neurotic, her overeating becomes compulsive eating. In future, it will be done in secret, in the kitchen, while she is preparing him a snack before he comes home.

The fact that it has become clandestine creates stress and tension, coupled with her resentment that he is monitoring her eating. She decides to 'punish' him by being completely unresponsive when it comes to love-making. She has always been taught it was wrong to express her anger so she bottles it up. Her feelings explode sooner or later in eating chaos. Although she tries to hide it from her husband, he soon notices that although food bills soar, there is never any food in the house. How can she explain where all the housekeeping money has gone? Of such stuff divorce is made. The children cannot understand why they are deprived of food by their ravenous mother. They whine. She is nervy, tensed up before another binge, and hits them. The next step might well be child-battering.

Greed is never an attractive trait in a relative or friend but it is nothing like as bad as the anti-social habits that a compulsive eater develops, which can revolt those close to her and ruin a relationship.

Una's husband understands her problem and when she was going through a stage of acute bingeing, he helped her by locking the kitchen door and hiding the key. Items like After-dinner mints were tucked away in his study out of temptation's way. Rosemary's fiancé has done everything in his power to ensure that she does not shop for or prepare food. He tries, in the ways he can understand, to help her with her problem although he finds it hard to understand why she cannot stop eating. But Rosemary resents it, imagining he is 'humouring' her when he sits down to the same sparse meal as her own, although he has no need to lose weight. Her usual reaction is to binge in order to spite him. 'I know it is destroying him, me and our relationship,' she told us. 'I know how much he hates to arrive home, come over and kiss me and feel my horribly distended stomach. But although I know all this and appreciate his attempts to understand me, the need to eat is stronger. It will win in the end.'

Not all men are like David or Michael. There are many who either will not or cannot understand the problem and come to believe they have married some kind of monster! Patricia's husband was marvellously supportive but even he could not tolerate a wife who had resorted to shoplifting in her desperate attempt to satisfy her craving for food. When she finally ended up in court, he walked out on her. He is a man of strong character and principle and sees her lack of control as a sign of weakness. Aware of this censure, the compulsive eater feels even more guilty, becomes even more sensitive and secretive and the vicious circle is reinforced. Marriage becomes a game of cat and mouse, as in Gillian's case. Her husband is very critical of her eating habits although even he is not fully aware of what is going on. She has reached the stage where she cannot eat in front of him and makes up for it by bingeing alone for comfort and reassurance. He sees her as fat and flabby, a very different woman from the one he married. He does not understand her problem and does not particularly want to try to. Her 'greed', as he sees it, will spoil their holiday yet again this year, when they will be living at close quarters for two weeks and he will not be able to escape her craving for food.

Joanna has learned to some extent to control her binges but she looks back on a time when she could never enjoy a holiday or social outing with her husband. He dreaded arriving home on a binge day as he knew what he would find: a tense woman whose moods swung erratically up and then down. Then she became tearful and desperate. Initially, she had tried to keep her secret from him with the result that she was constantly tense and unresponsive and he could not understand why. Now that she has 'come out' and he has had a glimpse of what goes on inside the 'cage', their marriage has improved although her eating problem is only partially solved and he continues to feel helpless and frustrated in dealing with it. The dreadful 'game' continues with a woman preparing snacks for her husband while taking every opportunity to be alone in the kitchen where she can cram food into her mouth. She cannot now bake him his favourite cake without first swallowing half the ingredients.

The Robins family, Derek, Lynn and their children, seem a happy and united group of people to the outside world. No one knows what goes on behind the front door of 43 Acacia Road and how Lynn's moods are undermining the domestic lives of Derek and their two daughters. He is saddened by the increasing occasions where there is no 'jolly wife' to greet him on his return from the office. He is baffled by her condition which he still finds hard to believe exists because he has never seen her binge. He only hears about it afterwards. And even then he has to prise it out of her as in the following, typical dialogue:

Derek: What's up, darling?
Lynn: Nothing's up.
Derek: You look as depressed as hell. Something's wrong.
Lynn: I feel very depressed.
Derek: Darling, I hear this so often. Can't you tell me

what's depressing you?

Lynn: Oh Derek, I've been eating – eating a lot! I've eaten lots of food and I can't stop.

Derek: Why do you think you do it? If we could talk, really talk, we might be able to work it out.

Lynn: It's no use. You don't understand.

Derek: But I want to try. I want to help you.

Such conversations are wearing away the fabric of their marriage. Derek loves his wife but he watches her grow away from him, increasingly lost in her private labyrinth. She has never been a very spontaneous, collaborative woman but, of late, her attitude of being always on the defensive and expecting not to be listened to has broken down communication between them. Derek is physically and mentally weary of it all. He is a hard-working man and all he wants is serenity when he comes home. But he is at his wits' end to know what to do as questioning Lynn only makes her more illogical. It has reached the point when he dreads going away on a short, unavoidable business trip, as he knows that his wife will become depressed, binge and be waiting to reproach him when he returns.

'Where did I go wrong?' is a frequent pathetic plea of parents, confronted by a child who develops an eating problem in her teens. As many mothers have experienced, food and the act of eating represents a battleground early on in their offspring's life. But if it can be accepted as a part of normal development, it usually dies away as the child finds his or her feet. An adolescent who develops a lack of control over food is another and much more daunting prospect that can have a devastating effect on family life. While she may be filled with compassion, a mother feels bewildered and frustrated because she cannot help, and brothers and sisters come to resent the member of the family who greedily demands as much attention as the food she devours.

Margaret, a very immature nineteen-year-old, has used her habit of vomiting as a form of blackmail, reminiscent of the *Just William* character, Violet Elizabeth Bott, who threatened to scream and continue to scream until she was 'thick' if she did not have what she wanted. When you are only three, you feel mother is all powerful and can change the world. This is what Margaret expects her unfortunate mother to do these days. From her diary, the following domestic incident points up the disruptive effect of her family. Her mother and sister were having breakfast with Margaret, prior to an outing to a nearby town. They wanted Margaret to go with them because they did not want to leave her on her own, as they were fearful she would start eating. Margaret sensed their fears and, resenting their concern, refused point blank to go with them. Finally, overcome by yet another battle, her mother broke down and cried, accusing her daughter of not trying and certainly of not caring about her family. Margaret described how she sat in silence, very upset, and after they had left, she 'cried and cried and then the usual happened. I felt so sad at being unable to cope with Mummy being upset. I knew I would binge.' For this family, Margaret's eating disorder, her bingeing and purging, is the pivot around which they must all revolve. Her mother identifies with her to a greater degree but her sisters, gregarious young girls, are apt to become impatient. They prefer to go out and leave her to cope as best she can. The situation is very much like having a cuckoo in the nest, a demanding, overgrown child who, in spite of their love for her, ruins the lives of everyone else. She cannot move out of adolescence into other mature relationships beyond the home and the responsibility weighs increasingly heavily upon her parents who have the other girls to consider.

'I believe that one aspect of this eating disorder comes about as a means of punishing parents,' a clergyman told us, in an attempt to understand his daughter's problem. The Reverend John Edwards is a deeply caring man who, in the course of his ministry, has worked with people suffering from alcoholic addiction. He expressed strong feelings of guilt where his youngest daughter, Lily, is concerned and believes that he did not give her enough attention when she was small. Lily suffers from somewhat unstable blood sugar levels, one of the possible causes of compulsive eating. What she needs is good, sound nutrition. The Reverend Edwards has no need to feel guilty, but this has not prevented his daughter's problem causing much sorrow and disruption within the family.

Although the Reverend Edwards admits that his work kept him busy when the children were young and did not permit him to devote much time to them, he points out that his other sons and daughters are self-assured, well-balanced young people, thus indicating that Lily is 'different'. He believes that the stress she suffered in trying to keep up with her siblings may have precipitated her problem and he feels guilty that he took a 'fairly strong line' with her when she was not doing well at school. The family has been very concerned over their daughter, seeking medical advice, which has not helped very much. Since we have advised on nutrition, however, she has improved and has managed to step out into the world. A steady boyfriend has taken the pressure off home life. But the Reverend Edwards added that until the door was locked every time the family left the kitchen, food, intended for the others, continued to vanish from the refrigerator. Guilt is a difficult commodity to deal in. There could be a much easier exchange of give and take within this family if everyone came to terms with the fact that Lily's problem results from a metabolic imbalance. Perhaps the solution sounds too simple!

Should parents feel guilty because one of their children develops an eating problem and seems locked away in a 'cage' from which they feel helpless and hopeless to extract her? Stephanie is convinced that none of her family understands her while her mother soul-searches for the trigger which set off her daughter's eating disorder. She worries constantly. As a helpless onlooker, she has watched her daughter gradually enter the 'cage' during an unsatisfactory relationship. At 5 feet 8 inches, Stephanie was not fat, weighing around 9½ stone, but a shorter, slightly built boyfriend convinced her she was large. She dieted until she had reduced her weight to 7½ stone and at that point the couple split up. Stephanie began to eat and eat such enormous quantities that, within two months, her weight had shot up a staggering 4 stone. Now she eats compulsively and never with the family, but her mother has spied on her and watched her gorge. She involves herself in disastrous relationships and a bewildered Mrs P. looks on, endeavouring to understand and help. She asks herself, 'Where did I go wrong?'

The very people you imagine would help, family and close friends, sense a mystery, see strange behaviour occur and feel that the person they love is retreating behind the bars into an isolated world. They try to reach her, try to enter into some kind of dialogue but are repulsed and, more often than not, feel inadequate to cope with this distressing condition. And the compulsive eater, herself, realizing the effect she is having and the burden she is putting on those who love her, cannot communicate to them the hell in which she is living.

As Margaret said: 'I told my family last year that I did not think things could get any worse, but they have. I can't cope with my family and they can't cope with me but I expect them to because I feel so alone and need help.'

Joanna: 'I know it is upsetting my home life. I don't want to destroy my family but I am because I can't control myself. I need help.'

Lynn: 'No one understands what I am going through.'

Claire: 'Can you help me? I am alone in this and I'm desperate.'

They all need help but their loved ones can only look on. They do not know how to turn the key.

3 Reasons Why

What causes compulsive eating? – the childhood roots of eating disorders

Why does someone become out of tune with herself and out of tune with the world around her? When does the 'war' with herself begin? Perhaps in her personal history we can find the first clue to her eating problems, helplessness and hopelessness and her sense of being of lesser value than *them*. Maybe we can begin to discover why and how she first climbed onto that destructive carousel.

Food is a natural and essential part of our lives. It is probably our first and last gratification and comfort. But it is not difficult for it to become a highly emotive issue between mother and baby that turns meal times into a battlefield. The hyper-sensitive mother, intent on urging Junior to 'see the pattern' at the bottom of the plate, is giving food too much importance. And the child who wins his mother's approval this way is learning a behaviour pattern that may equate 'good' with polishing off every scrap.

Feeding time for the newborn baby, according to child expert Penelope Leach, should be nothing short of 'gentle bliss'. Tenderly, he has to be taught to understand the difference between displeasure and pleasure and how the latter is created in his tiny, limited world by learning to suck and thus finding food and comfort. At this stage, he is purely an instinctual being and 'greed' does not apply. There are some babies who simply burn up their food with greater efficiency and others whose metabolism demands more fuel. A baby 'knows' exactly how much he needs and when he needs it. Frequently, however, a mother will become worried and over-anxious and her approach can confuse her child even at this early stage. If only she could relax and make feeding an enjoyable experience for the two of them, not forgetting the cuddles while the child sucks.

Such a natural camaraderie of demand and supply discourages the possibility of a baby taking in too much and becoming fat, although the likelihood of this happening increases if he is bottle-fed. However staunch the belief in the 'bonny baby' image, overfeeding – which is much easier to do with bottle and supplements – is not a good idea and a mother who allows her child to become fat during the early months would do well to realize that he may be more prone to obesity later in life.

Weaning, in terms of its effects on later likes or dislikes of food and the act of eating, is the most traumatic experience after that of birth. We are pushed out of that warm, primeval cradle into the cold world and not very long after the beautiful breast or soft teat is snatched away from us and a hard spoon shoved into our mouths. Again, it can be an over-anxious, perhaps first-time mother, grimly determined that the baby will grow up strong and healthy, who creates a problem for them both. Look at it from the infant's point of view. He cannot make out what he is supposed to do with his spoon. He feels the discomfort he has learnt signals hunger and he cries for breast or bottle. If she is wise, his mother can continue to keep the business of eating pleasurable. She will never force food into his mouth but gently offer tiny samples of things, finding out by trial and error whether the baby likes them or not. Tiny he may be, but he is an individual with a right to preferences. If he is respected, he will come around to the idea that what is on the spoon is just as delicious as what was in the bottle or breast. Overridden by a mother who 'knows best', he may well revert, in later life and in times of stress, to what we call 'nursery' carbohydrates: milky, sloppy items, such as creamed rice pudding or tinned custard.

It is also important to allow a child to feed himself at quite an early age. Many children's feeding problems arise from the fact that the mother seems unwilling to see her child grow up and continues to feed him long after it is necessary. Understandably, because this is such a time-consuming period, she may well want to avert the dreadful mess a baby is capable of when allowed to take over the feeding process himself: rice pudding on the floor and the walls and ice cream all over his face, anywhere it seems but in his mouth! But this desire to play with food is really a serious business. Messy it may be but it is important in the learning process. If it is a game of his choice he is comforted by the sensation that what he eats is under his control. If he feels his mother is pressurizing him his cues may become confused. Long after this weaning period is over and apparently forgotten a compulsive eater may continue to feel this lack of control over eating and must learn, as an adult, to break through this buried dependency and establish contact with his own body. Mothers must learn to trust a small child's instinct about how much he needs.

It is, of course, all very well to say 'relax' to the woman who has become obsessed by the fact that her offspring will not eat, or eats all the wrong foods. And he, sensitive to this anxiety, quickly learns to use food and the act of eating or not eating as a powerful weapon. Toddler tantrums are harrowing enough but such a situation can have far-reaching consequences. Habits established when very young can result in a 'picky' eater and at worst in the development of an eating disorder.

A common mistake is to confuse an endeavour to feed the child well so that he develops at a steady rate and is healthy, with the desire to teach him to behave 'properly'. The art is to learn to distinguish between the two. When you urge your son to eat up his greens like a good boy because they will make his hair curl, what issue are you raising? If you entangle discipline with meal times, you confuse a toddler who, instead of continuing in his own sweet instinctual way of knowing when he is not hungry or has had sufficient, comes to realize that here, at table, he has 'the power to command attention. This is heady ammunition for a developing child and he will use it time and again. If a mother offers adequate food and if a child is hungry he will answer the cue and eat. Failure to accept this situation can set up abnormal eating patterns early in life that will persist.

To examine just how true it is that a mother may give her child the responsibility for his eating habits, may let him dabble his fingers in his food, throw it about, starve himself for twenty-four hours and then devour packets of crisps, let us look at the surprising results of a research study carried out nearly fifty years ago. The aim was to discover what happened when young children were allowed to choose their own food without guidance from parents or dieticians. The results demonstrated clearly that babies and toddlers have an inbuilt appetite-control centre that regulates their food intake with a remarkable precision. It also showed that when they were given complete liberty to choose what they wanted to eat, how much and when they wanted to eat it, the long-term behaviour was to settle down to a perfect balance of nutrients. In the short term, of course, the child might eat practically nothing for a day and then cram in quantities of a single item, but only while his body was experimenting and adjusting. If he has never been allowed to experiment and experience extremes he will never learn this balance. Left to his own devices, trusted to 'know' what he is doing and being allowed to 'listen' to his eating cues, a child will grow up to have an appetite-control centre in perfect working order. But if a mother forces food into the child's mouth when he turns his head away, that child will learn as effectively to override that exquisitely balanced system.

It is infuriating, of course, to have spent hours preparing something 'special' for finicky juvenile appetites and then to watch a child persistently push the food around the plate and announce that he does not 'like meat any more'. But to fly into a rage or display anxiety only exacerbates abnormal attitudes towards foods. It is far better to accept the fact that children should be allowed to have personal tastes and appetites rather than rigidly to insist on his eating up everything that is set in front of him. Putting yourself in the child's place sometimes helps to calm the situation. Would you like to have food you do not enjoy forced upon you? Would you not react to having someone help you to food you dislike or in a greater quantity than you feel you need? How would you feel if you were urged to eat when you were not hungry?

That is not to say that children should be discouraged from accepting the idea of eating at least some of the items everyone else is eating that day, nor should they expect that, having announced they have suddenly 'gone off' something, it will necessarily produce an alternative. Sometimes a child, who is worried about something, will go off his food to camouflage the real problem. It is the perceptive mother who maintains meal times as enjoyable, relaxed occasions so that if Johnny or Jane has had a bad school report it will not impinge on eating habits. Alternatively, a child may stuff himself with more food than is necessary when he is emotionally upset or uncertain of himself, thus setting up a response to food that will often continue when he is older.

Mary J. became a secret nibbler at the age of eight. She had been a heavy baby and sturdy toddler. An unkind remark from her school sports teacher kept her fat for the next twenty years. 'Mary is an energetic and agile child,' said the unthinking teacher. 'It is just a shame she looks like a balloon.' Mary loved sports and, in spite of her rounded little body, was a good gymnast. But expressing her joy on the trampoline had made her a laughing stock and so she retired into her shell. Because of this, she shunned gym classes at the age of eight and resorted to the larder where she ate to comfort herself. She took great care that no one ever saw her eating and even her loving, anxious mother could not understand how the happy little girl had become a withdrawn, quiet and increasingly plump child.

Mothers find it all too tempting to offer food as a reward

and withhold it as a punishment. But its habitual use in such situations can build up wrong associations. 'Finish up your meat and vegetables and then you can have this lovely ice cream' might seem like a magical formula to a despairing mother but the truth is that often it does not 'work'. If a child does not want that first course he will not eat it. As he comes to understand your ruse, the chances are he will begin to put too much emotional value onto that ice cream as a reward. Ice cream can be a nourishing item on a child's menu but it should not be offered because he has been a dutiful child. Childish, bad behaviour during the day should not be brought up while he is eating. And the punishment of sending a child to bed without his supper is not only inhumane but may well destroy the establishment of right attitudes towards food. Mothers who pursue such a course may find that their children grow up unable to distinguish between the need for food and other sensations and feelings of pleasure or sorrow. Hunger or satiety does not come into such a disordered eating pattern and they may well need outside signals to tell them when to eat and when to stop.

Hilde Bruch pointed out that sufferers from eating problems have often come from houses where their parents gave their children food or deprived them of it, for reasons that had no relation to a child's sensations of hunger or satiety. These parents may have found it difficult to show affection except by the gift of food, or it may have been offered to distract the child, even tranquillize it, by an otherwise occupied mother. Such mothers will have deprived their children of the ability to learn for themselves whether they are truly hungry. When they grow up, they will have suffered from two fundamental gaps in their education: of not being able to recognize real hunger, and of being deprived of a feeling of independence.

David has fought his compulsive eating problem for as long as he can remember. At twenty-nine, he gets up in the night to guzzle and finds Sunday the most problematic day of the week. Bored, he roams about the house and goes to the refrigerator for solace. He looks back to the time when he was five years old and broke both his legs, causing him to be bed-ridden for a long time. 'My mother smothered me with sympathy, not to mention sweets, home-made cakes and my favourite puddings. All she wanted was to keep me "happy" but all she succeeded in doing was to create my eating habits of today.' David quickly learned to use food to offset his boredom, induced by the enforced rest, and a pattern was set up throughout his growing years of an almost automatic giving on the part of his mother, and receiving on his own part, of a cake or sweets to ease any anxiety, whatever its cause.

It is possibly the emotional value put on sweets that makes them suspect quite apart from the sugar content. The mother, who produces a lollipop to 'make better' a bruised elbow or an unkind schoolfriend's remark, runs the risk of confusing a child's cues for eating. If sweets become a 'special case', linked with occasions of comforting, loving or solace-giving, he will come to look upon them as the only valid currency for all the slings and arrows of life. If a mother reduces their importance and treats them as just food, which occasionally forms part of a normal meal, they will come to represent only one aspect of the many nice things life has to offer.

Confused food cues over the sweets issue may begin psychologically but can result in upsetting the balance of biologically regulated mechanisms. David absorbed far too much of the sweet, sugary and carbohydrate-laden foods early in his life and these days turns to them to deal with the emotions of boredom, anxiety and frustration. Symbolically, he is giving himself a hug, using food as a comforter. We all need comfort, reassurance and love and no one more significantly than the baby and small child. New experiences and sensations come at him from all sides and often they seem incomprehensible. He needs you to translate and define emotions, such as loving. The more he can feel he is loved, the greater his capacity to give and accept love during his life. Loving a child does not mean showering him with sweets and treats nor depriving him completely of them. It means developing a calm, relaxed attitude towards your child and an understanding so that he will develop a natural appetite control. Every parent would like to feel they had not ruined the normal link between hunger and enjoying food for their child and that knowing how to eat in company had been taught by example and not by bribes or punishments. Thus food and eating do not become inextricably linked in his mind with love and discipline.

The problem of compulsive eating often comes to a head at adolescence. In any circumstances, this is a traumatic time when the end of childhood is indicated by very obvious body changes and there are demands for independence. It is a time of becoming aware of one's physical power and sexual attractiveness to the opposite sex, of learning who we are and what our value is. If we add to all this the probability of puppy-fat problems, the anxiety and stress levels are high. And if, as a baby and small child, the adolescent has never learnt correct hunger cues, when faced with these pressures he or she may very well go over the top.

Few of us can look back on our teenage years as being of unadulterated pleasure. Overnight, it seemed, life stopped being a game with all the odds in one's favour and became a serious, somewhat frightening affair. There was no one to guarantee instant popularity, or to 'kiss it better' if a mistake was made. One famous actress saw the years between seventeen and twenty as the most miserable of her life. She began to eat compulsively, was fat and had acne. 'I was always hopelessly in love with someone but never told them because I thought they would laugh at me,' she said. 'I suppose I was growing up and wanted to shed the sweet little girl image. But I saw life as work for the first time and I was scared I couldn't deal with it.' Sometimes, like Mary, a youngster will retreat further and further into taking what seems to be the easy way out. Because of her early snub by the gym mistress, Mary had grown up without ambition, convincing herself that she was not one of *them* and would never do anything with her life. She was content to tick over, hiding behind her office desk and eating huge lunches to blot out all feeling. 'If children's early enthusiasm is dampened down and they are ridiculed, they become as I did,' she said, 'so self-conscious that it literally paralyses them. I was fat but I didn't move a finger to do anything about it. I focused my life on my parents, my undemanding job and food. That way, I decided I should never be hurt again.'

Some teenagers learn to cope with their eating problems by turning the joke on themselves in an attempt to attract the popularity they crave. The image of the jolly hearty eater is a familiar stereotype, which is often deceiving. Food for such young compulsive eaters may well be an easily obtainable tranquillizer while, underneath, they remain tense and insecure. A more realistic picture would be that of a young person who is obese because of uncontrolled eating, and who finds it hard to make friends and adapt to new pressures. Anxious because they feel they are 'different', they become depressed and the vicious circle is completed as they turn again to the familiar and comforting effect of food.

Iris was twelve years old when her parents exposed her to such a traumatic experience that her previously normal and small appetite became distorted into using food for solace. She was a very shy child who had been accustomed to going everywhere with her mother and was completely unprepared for her parents' abandonment of her. One day, they took her on a 'visit' to a boarding-school. Later, following an invitation to the headmistress's room for tea, they left her there. 'At first it didn't register,' says Iris, for whom the event remains imprinted on her mind. 'I have a vivid recollection of that tea table, of the food I had to eat after my father pressed some pocket-money into my hand and said goodbye. The reality hit me next morning when I awoke and sobbed my heart out. I lost my appetite but at that school you were made to stay at table until you had eaten everything. There was also a punishment for homesick girls: you were sent to bed without food.' Today, Iris eats compulsively. The loss of love, as she interpreted her parents' action, was replaced by food that she learned to use to cushion the blow and soothe her. As Iris learned quite early in life, periods of physical or emotional closeness are transitory. The baby is fed, cuddled but then laid down in his cot while his mother goes away to do other necessary jobs. The toddler, attached to mother's apron strings for several years, is suddenly left in the school playground with strangers. Iris's extremely close and apparently loving home environment was shattered and she was pushed prematurely out of the nest.

One of our earliest, learned lessons is that we run the risk of suffering some kind of loss if we are close to another human being. Lovers know that sense of 'it's too good to last'. We shall never again experience that all-enveloping sense of unity we had at our mother's breast. For some, the lesson is taught gently and wisely, for others, it is harsh and traumatic. Some of us can accept and cope; but some of us learn to use food as a substitute for those feelings of comfort and warmth. Early family attitudes can provide fertile ground for eating disorders if the giving or refusing of food has been linked with approval or disapproval, loving or rejection. It is understandable that, when sex is added to this longing for intimacy, the flames of an obsession are fanned because of the fear of being abandoned. The conflict between the desire to yield and the fear that afterwards we may suffer, is often reflected in an eating disorder which uses food for comfort. Many compulsive eaters sound almost like Victorian brides when asked what they think about when making love: 'I lie on my back and count calories.' 'I wanted to enjoy it,' Iris told us, 'but my mind seemed blocked by thoughts of food. It is always my priority and controls all my actions.'

While we believe that there is a minority of women who use obesity as a protection against sex, we cannot agree with the assumptions made in the book *Fat is a Feminist Issue*, which imply that women make themselves fat and therefore sexually unattractive because it is the only way they can persuade men to take them seriously. There may be some women who do this but we have not met them. Out of the many cases we have seen, there has been only one who expressed a fear of becoming slim and even she has controlled her eating and has lost several stone. The women we see hate their fat. They want to be slim, not for men's sake but for their own. We would rather suggest that some women eat compulsively and become obsessed with food because they are aware of their inability to enter fully into a sexual relationship and so attempt to fill that sense of vacuum with food.

However chaotic their eating habits are, there is a 'pattern' of sorts and emotions that are familiar to compulsive eaters, even if they are negative ones. To expose their sexuality, or to step outside their often rigid personality, is to take the risk of rejection and its attendant emotions. Said Carol: ' I had a boyfriend I was crazy about and I longed to go to bed with him but I imagined I looked awful. I refused, therefore, and he told me I was frigid. It goes without saying that I turned to my familiar comforter, food.'

We have seen that, as our compulsive eater begins to achieve control, she develops more confidence in sexual matters. But change can be frightening, even if it is a change for the better. It may mean that these women outgrow their partners, becoming too active in a relationship where the man had previously assumed a protective, fatherly and understanding role. They may, albeit unconsciously, have chosen such a partner when in the throes of compulsive eating because the relationship was relatively asexual.

According to Peter Dally and Joan Gomez, the authors of *Obesity and Anorexia Nervosa: a Question of Shape*, many of the young women who hide behind compulsive eating are unable to form warm and satisfying sexual relationships and they eat for compensation. Their fear of rejection, which in their eyes is deserved, appears to have shaped their social pattern. Even if they do find a partner and marry they are inclined to remain detached and unfulfilled and eating is used to fill that sense of a gap.

Maureen blames her husband because she binges between seven and ten in the evening. That is the time Oliver works an evening shift, and they are the hours when she is alone and lonely in the house. Irrationally, she resents him. It is his 'fault' and although she loves him, she refuses him sex to 'punish' him. But Maureen craves love and needs sex. Four nights a week, she goes out to pick up a man and goes to bed with him. The aftermath of guilt sends her to the larder for reassurance. Oliver knows about her eating problem and it will not be long before he knows about those other men in Maureen's life.

Sometimes there seems to be a kind of conspiracy where both partners focus on her compulsive eating rather than face up to her fear of sex. The man remains protective and undemanding, helping his wife to continue to be dependent and inadequate. There is no hope here unless they grow up or split up. Lorraine was a fractious baby and very difficult with her food. Her mother became over-anxious as the problem continued throughout her toddler years and, when Lorraine was nine, she was sent away to boarding-school. Here she continued to be withdrawn and unco-operative. Later, however, she met Paul and fell in love, finding sex enjoyable, while he found her a passionate lover. After they were married, she began to imagine he was looking at other women and she developed a feeling of worthlessness. She began to binge/purge constantly, asking Paul to help her control the problem and arguing with him when he tried, although he confessed that he was completely bewildered by it all. Their love-making became non-existent.

Lorraine had found sex 'good' and, probably for the first time in her life, asserted herself in a positive way. Then the fear of separation and loss crept in. She became afraid of getting close to Paul in case she was hurt and so bottled up her feelings inside her. Lorraine's thought pattern went something like this: 'I am worthless. No one could love me and, anyway, it is foolish to trust a man. I shan't show my love or my grief and fear. I'll stay on the defensive and not let him near me.' As many a compulsive eater can understand, Lorraine found that her food obsession, which she used to repress her painful feelings, had isolated her. Compulsive eating is a painful and lonely experience but at least food is familiar and that had enabled her to handle feelings of anger and resentment.

When, for some reason, you dampen down your normal outlets for love, comfort, cuddles and hugs, you need to create a substitute. This can manifest itself as a physical or emotional problem as in an eating disorder and seems to be completely unrelated. When you begin to feel secure, and to love yourself, the problem can come under control, for the mind and body are so closely connected. Eating compulsively occurs not only after sexual rejection but also after sexual abandonment and this may come about because of the sufferer's penchant for choosing the wrong sort of person as a lover. The hurt, loss of warmth and lack of solace make her move away and smoke a cigarette, have a drink or, in the case of Jenny, go downstairs and make herself a doorstep of a cheese sandwich. 'I don't understand myself or my compulsion to eat at times like this,' she told us. 'It's not that I'm hungry. I feel resentful somehow, as if I am trying to satisfy myself, to fill an empty space.'

Even with fulfilment each of us anticipates the loss, the inevitable drawing away of a lover after intimacy. We may say we are not 'in the mood', using ciphers to explain that tension which coming close to someone creates. Or we may say we are 'too tired'. Certainly, if you do suffer from compulsive eating you will be so physically tensed up with anger, fear and grief and so emotionally preoccupied that you *will* be too tired for love-making. Compulsive eating can thus be doubly destructive. It can keep you feeling inadequate and worthless, and can get in the way of a fulfilling relationship, which could allay those feelings of inadequacy.

Grace was terrified of sex. While in hospital, undergoing treatment for her eating disorder, she met a man who was an alcoholic. She had dreamed of marrying, when all problems would vanish and she would live happily ever after. 'I had got over my fear of sex although I wasn't the hottest thing in bed. But he told me my body did nothing for him. He was the only person I met with whom I could relax and make love without needing a drink. But two sick people cannot make a marriage.' Grace has had affairs since, but never makes love except when she is very drunk. 'If you get drunk, you lose your inhibitions about your body and you can forget your fear of rejection. The problem is that alcohol also reduces my control over eating.'

One solution to the fear of rejection is to go in for the superficial type of relationship. We have been startled by the admissions of apparently 'moral' women who have openly confessed to promiscuity. There was Naomi who was not mad about sex but who needed to be loved and made to feel wanted. She was fat, she loved her husband and she did not want to read disgust and rejection on his face. But she did not mind going to bed with other men because, as ships in the night, their reaction was not important. As time went by, however, her attitude hardened and she began to group all men together as being untrustworthy and became resentful because her lovers had used her body. She has now directed her resentment onto the nearest male, her husband, who loves her. Naomi is now riding high on that feast/fast merry-go-round.

Mary was a success story. She grew up and became attracted to a man who was much older than herself. Boys of her own age ignored her and only Tony bothered to find out about the interesting girl living inside that fat body. She warmed to the security and support he gave her. But although it seemed right for her at the time, deep inside she felt dissatisfied, sensing that she was making do. All her life she had settled for a quiet existence, resigning herself not to expect much. 'Getting by' still seemed sensible but her life was empty. They seldom made love and Tony was sexually undemanding so that Mary turned back to food as the familiar provider of satisfaction and solace. 'I kept on eating because I was afraid that if I stopped I'd have nothing to fill that space.' Mary began to control her eating after we had met her and she started to feel in command of her body. Gradually, her attitude towards Tony changed. It was fortunate that he was mature enough to understand and accept this, and they agreed to part.

Belinda is an extremely attractive twenty-eight-year-old air hostess who, in common with many compulsive eaters, sees herself as ugly and uninteresting. When she was a child, her mother instilled into her the notion that 'nice girls do not enjoy sex'. Her friends are liberated young women who enjoy life. Belinda is terrified of having anything more than a superficial relationship in case the man 'finds out and thinks me virginal and boring'. She wants to be 'nice' as her parents taught her to be and has resolved her conflict by turning to food for comfort. Belinda is driven to please other people. She feels insecure, she does not love herself and cannot love anyone else. If she would allow herself to be sensual, to believe that 'nice girls' can risk losing control, her sexual happiness could be increased and her eating decreased.

Many of the compulsive eaters we see are not happy with their bodies. Imprisoned in their 'fat' image, they cannot let themselves go and enjoy sex. This feeling does not apply only to women but to men, too. David's mother gave him lollipops to make his broken legs 'better'. When he grew up, he continued to eat compulsively and his weight ruined his sex life. He could make love only when the light was out and the sheets were pulled right up over himself and his wife. She began to develop constant 'headaches' and he felt equally disinclined because of the sheer effort involved in love-making with his huge body. But he also became depressed, which made him eat more. The couple have now split up temporarily while David attempts to fight his compulsion.

The woman who is confident and happy about herself is attractive and moderate thinness or fatness fades in importance. But as we know, self-respect and self-love are qualities that are missing in many compulsive eaters. Favourite fairy tales always contain a message of hope. The frog becomes a prince. That which was lost is found again. But the real life story of the compulsive eater often seems to promise no such happy endings. There is nothing or no one to 'make it up' to them so they comfort themselves with food. Sadly, the problem can be passed on to the sufferer's children.

Leslie remembers the first year of her marriage when she really 'went to town on food. My mother always kept me out of the kitchen. Now there was no check on me. My husband was away a lot but when he was home I felt I should feed him up. Sunday was our favourite eating day. By evening we'd feel bloated but so cosy and contented.' When Leslie became pregnant it was easy to convince herself she hadn't a problem; she was simply 'eating for two'. But her prenatal classes were humiliating because everyone stared and made jokes about her. Leslie felt worthless, deprived even of the joy of her first baby. At four years old, her son is already showing signs of the obesity that dogged Leslie's mother and compounded Leslie's compulsive eating, although she tries, not very successfully, to change the pattern of eating in the family.

As a child grows towards adolescence, the relationship between her and her mother can become strained, especially if the father is busy or is unable to reaffirm both to mother and daughter that they are beloved in their own right. A mother who has become insecure and depressed by thoughts of her fading attraction may be impatient, resentful or even jealous of her daughter and this can sometimes precipitate the daughter's diet/bingeing pattern. Sometimes this is due not only to the mother's depression but also to a power struggle going on between the parents. One of our compulsive eaters remembers her mother as a very beautiful and elegant woman who never showed any affection towards her daughter. Her father she found 'much more fun'.

Delia's mother was a finicky eater and often locked herself

in the bathroom in order to be sick. 'I think my mother resented me in a way,' Delia said. 'If I started to put on weight, I was consoled by her saying, "Have my skirt or dress, dear," or "Have another syrup sponge." She was a size eight and I believe she did this on purpose to make me feel worse. I know I wasn't wanted. Mother admitted jumping off the kitchen table when I was on the way, although the family passed it off as a joke. She made a rotten mother but a good grandmother.'

Family food habits are a powerful force in preserving family traditions, and familiar foods give reassurance, comfort, a sense of warmth and of belonging to a unit. The taste or appearance of sweet foods plays a very emotive role. Our language is littered with expressions and phrases that imply that something sweet in the mouth is analogous to a 'good' quality. Rupert Brooke, looking back nostalgically, asked if there was honey still for tea. It is difficult to say whether the man who adores cakes and sweet puddings is obeying a physiological or biochemical need or whether he remembers other, happier times in childhood and youth when he drops yet another lump of sugar into his coffee. A mother coaxes her child with promises of ice cream; the compulsive eater promises herself a big chunk of gâteau as a reward when she has had a hard day. In our culture, a cup of tea is invested with almost magical properties. Our compulsive eater uses certain foods to provide this 'tea and sympathy', this comfort that is much more than physical and may have sentimental connections. The depressed, unsatisfied woman eating muesli and Christmas pudding at two in the morning for that feeling of warmth and comfort may well be craving other times and other places associated with food or other satisfactions.

Can we put down all bad eating habits to deprivation in childhood or adolescence? Surely, most of us have been deprived in some way or another and yet we do not all have an eating disorder. Each of us is the product not only of what has been done to us but also of our own reaction to it, so that an intolerably deprivating or difficult family situation may produce compulsive eating in one person and not in another.

Junk food and its effects

Ever since we were born, our brains have been busy coupling food with emotions and performing a sort of computer-dating service so that, very early in our lives, eating became no longer a matter of 'pure' hunger, but was linked with all kinds of associations and fantasies. When we are bored, frustrated, tense or in need of comfort, our personal computer may suggest that food is the answer. Our tastes and attitudes have become established but now even though we may be convinced, logically speaking, that certain items are not 'good' for us, that we 'shouldn't have them', outside influences and temptations are increasingly brought to bear. Not only have we formed a pattern of eating habits, organized by early and individual routines, but we have also established the habit of eating nowadays at the wrong times, the wrong choice of food because other people are eating it.

Think of it: the hamburger bars, fast food eateries and the takeaways of every description that have sprung up in every town in the country. And as many a jaundiced restaurateur will tell you, they are the places that make the money. In the supermarket, the shelves are packed with convenience foods, 'television snacks' and bite-sized confectionery you can nibble, suck or chew. It has surely never been so simple, physically to lay your hands on food – and food that is binge material.

As every compulsive eater knows to her cost, if she has to halt in the middle of a craving because a foodstuff requires preparation, she will pass over that in favour of something that is instant. Junk food is there, and is her downfall. While you peel or bake there is time for reflection; but instant food is ready to be wolfed down. Normal physiology balances what we put into our body with what we put out, in terms of energy. But outside forces are threatening this balance. Whether we go out to work in an office, factory, shop or keep house, our labours require less and less physical effort. Our leisure-time activities are becoming more passive, too. What do we do? We use much less energy than ever before and occupy ourselves with eating instant, convenience, fast and junk foods, while we stare at the television or video screen. We do not grow these foods for ourselves, nor do we gather or prepare them. We open a tin or a packet or, easier still, go out to a fast fooderie, hamburger bar or takeaway. Food is playing an increasingly important role in our lives; we are preoccupied by it. No longer is it confined to meal times but overspills into other times during the day. Snacks, breaks and nibbles cut through the monotony and the vendor of the fast and easy food will not let us forget that. And yet, as Peter Hudson, author of *Why Die Young?* points out, when we consume a greater quantity of food than we can satisfactorily digest, we clog and retard the whole metabolic process.

Take the case of Hilary, nineteen years old, and a typist with a firm of solicitors. She must be familiar to many of us. Hilary skips family breakfast because she always feels tired in the morning and lies in bed until the last minute. She looks forward to 'elevenses', to nibbling biscuits with her sugary coffee. She spends most of her lunch hour window-shopping and then darts into the nearest bakery for a cream bun or Danish pastry, which probably contains, among its other delights, a preservative, flavour enhancer, mould inhibitor, emulsifying agent, stabilizer and antioxidant. But it all slips down with a glass of coke.

A friend suggested to Hilary that she went to a lunchtime keep-fit class and she did try it once or twice, but could not be bothered to keep it up. In the evening, when she feels too tired to go out, her supper might consist of a Cornish pasty, mushy processed peas and chips followed by a dessert she can whip up in seconds, which is packed full of more synthetic items. Afterwards, she sits down to watch television with a box of chocolates and a bottle of fizzy lemonade within easy reach. As time goes by, Hilary feels increasingly tired, full of the 'dreads', shaky and on edge. Worst of all, she finds she cannot stop herself eating. She goes to her doctor who suggests a restricted diet and, to help her along, he writes out prescriptions for slimming pills, diuretics and tranquillizers. Hilary's compulsive eating has crept up on her. She became used to eating junk foods until she craved them. The drugs the doctor carelessly scribbled out for her and the complete lack of exercise can only exacerbate her problem.

It reminds us of another compulsive eater, Pauline, who does not mind Sundays 'if I've got my tablets. I am so full of tablets I feel apologetic all the time,' she told us. 'I'm hooked on food, hooked on tablets and I never have a cigarette out of my mouth. I feel like a junkie.' Pauline's doctor is wiser than some and has refused to prescribe any more appetite suppressants, but she manages to buy them privately. This takes a large chunk out of her wage packet, which results in yet another vicious circle. She thinks she cannot afford to buy good wholefood for a balanced diet and continues to exist on sugary drinks and junk foods, blotting out the symptoms that recur with tranquillizers and anti-depressants.

We all have now the ability to eat indiscriminately and unwisely. According to Peter Hudson: 'Given the power to think, man seems to have lost most of his instinctive powers. He lives and eats by intellect rather than instinct, and when man traded instinct for intellect he made a disastrous bargain as far as his health was concerned. Instinct would never direct him to adulterated, devitalized foods, starches, artificial sweets and foods high in harmful fats, yet his intellect does.' We have become accustomed to the sort of food which we know, deep down, we should not eat. Instinctively, many of us search for a diet that is more closely linked to the soil, a diet that is low in calories and high in fresh wholefoods. But exterior temptations tell us it is easier, faster and much more *fun* to eat those refined carbohydrate, chemical-ridden foodstuffs. We are encouraged until we become addicted to them.

Some compulsive eaters recognize this conflict but it does not prevent them from continuing to eat these foods. As Margaret said: 'The foods I binge on are the foods I would never normally eat. When I binge, I tend to eat foods I know I shouldn't touch and don't really like; fried and greasy foods, snack foods, crisps, chocolates and fizzy drinks, which I know are bad for you and fattening, too.' In theory, none of us approves of junk foods. It is fashionable to condemn the food additives (some two thousand permitted items in Britain), chemicals, sugar consumption, processing and refining that goes on today. In a half-hearted way, we may try to change our eating habits, but it is very difficult when every supermarket shelf seems to conspire against it. 'I'm too tired' or 'I really haven't the time' tends to be our response when a change to a healthier diet is suggested.

These feelings of not wishing to bother to make radical changes are part of yet another vicious circle. If our leisure-time activities are becoming more passive, if we feel too fatigued to make the effort, either to exercise or alter the way in which we eat, the 'dead foods' we continue to eat may well be responsible for perpetuating that tiredness and disinclination. If you continually sup on a 'chemical soup', as one nutritionist described many processed food items, your energy will be sapped up. And to complete this 'eighties cocktail', when the sad results of junk food diets send you to the doctor, slimming pills, diuretics and tranquillizers will certainly not help a compulsive-eating problem but will only upset the balance more. According to Peter Hudson: 'Irrefutable evidence suggests that many thousands of people are suffering from drug-induced diseases of which the science of nutrition attacks the root cause by nourishing the body so that it re-achieves that balance.'

Not everyone succumbs, of course. *They* seem to be able to get away with a less than favourable diet, and to survive this murder in the kitchen. But for *us*, who are more susceptible, when the right balance of a mix of good foods is lost, we lose our way. *We* binge. We are not helpless, hopeless victims. We do not have to follow the diet of the Western world. But it takes a lot of effort to change. Many of us take the soft option and believe we can minimize our symptoms by the use of drugs. Women like Angela who 'controlled' her compulsive eating, as she described it to us, until we discovered that her method was to take sleeping tablets at five in the evening. Even so, she has become used to them and her cravings have begun to break through this drug-induced sleep, which makes her night eating ten times worse. She is sufficiently awake to make it to the larder, too dopey to register what she eats. Angela has stepped up the dose but there is a limit to the number of tablets she can take.

Researchers looking at the changing pattern of illness have discovered that many of the ailments we take for granted are extremely rare in those nations where food is still unprocessed and unrefined. Such communities also continue, until late in life, to work hard on the land. While in the West we have successfully combated the diseases due to malnutrition, we are developing others attributable to dysnutrition – problems that have come about where food may be plentifully available but it does not supply the right balance of nutrients. Another major factor in this life style is our lack of regular exercise, which results in the sapping of energy, upsets the digestive function and accentuates tension and stress. The compulsive eater is swamped in refined carbohydrates and yet remains deprived and the body seeking blindly for what it needs, binges. What does she do? She pops pills and binges again!

When you eat white bread, white rice or any of the refined and processed cereal foods, the result is that the metabolic traffic is snarled up. The extent to which this happens depends on the percentage of such deficient food in your diet. And if you comfort yourself with the labels telling you that such and such an item is enriched, we must disillusion you. The standard procedure for white flour is to remove numerous, naturally occurring nutrients and, until recently, replace them with three B vitamins, vitamin D, calcium and iron salts. At the moment, the Committee on Medical Aspects of Food Policy is debating whether the addition of calcium is still necessary because, it says, vitamins B1 and B3 can be obtained from other foods and inorganic food is poorly absorbed anyway. Nutritionally, this is not important because the addition of chalk, inorganic iron and synthetic vitamins to white flour can hardly improve an already devitalized product. You truly need all the nutrients in a natural form. A deficiency of even one can endanger the balance of your body.

Picture your body as a car's combustion engine, which uses vitamins as the sparking plugs, and you begin to see how these wonderful, minute nutrients work for us. Vitamins energize and regulate our metabolism through enzyme systems, keeping us functioning harmoniously at optimum levels. Together with minerals, they do not in themselves provide energy, the carbohydrates, fats and proteins do that, but *only* when the sparking plugs release them.

One example is the important vitamin B6, which can keep the nerves relaxed and can prevent muscular fatigue, particularly in those suffering from the cravings caused by pre-menstrual tension. Another is magnesium. Both are non-existent in refined wheat. The importance of a well-balanced diet is evident and all the vitamin tablets in the world cannot make up for that nice balance of nutrients obtainable from a mixed diet of unprocessed foods. Some of our twentieth-century *angst* must be due not only to the increased stresses of life but also to our habitually bad choice of food. The inexplicable apprehensions, the fears and phobias that accompany depression and anxiety, can be greatly alleviated by an eating plan low in refined carbohydrates and rich in good, fresh foods.

Some interesting studies in America, backed by British evidence, are revealing that foods deficient in nutrients may subtly alter our behaviour. This research into the link between food and behaviour is still at a somewhat tentative stage but it seems there is little doubt that 'we are what we eat', mentally as well as physically. One fascinating viewpoint is to look at criminal tendencies as being the result not so much of bad character as of a biochemical imbalance. And the fact that reliable findings are relatively sparse has not discouraged more enlightened doctors from applying these dietary theories on the principle that they seem to work. According to one expert, if you are under stress, one of the best ways of dealing with it is to eat healthy foods. Time and again, he has noted the psychological changes that can be brought about by different food.

Are these people honestly saying that a helping of brown rice every day keeps muggings away? Consider the experiments carried out by the director of the American New Life Foundation Trust, the Reverend Vic Ramsey. He and his wife weaned young drug addicts off their diet of junk and convenience food and instead fed them fresh wholefood. They noted marked changes in the youngsters' behaviour patterns including less aggression and violence. Alexander Schauss, a psychologist who is principally interested in criminality, conducted a study in 1977 that looked for a relationship between diet and deviancy. His conclusion was that an extremely unbalanced diet in which milk provided most of the protein could lead to an imbalance in the types of amino acids essential to the synthesis of some neurotransmitters and that this might affect behaviour. He has persuaded a number of State prison boards in America to change the diet of inmates and this has produced some drastic results.

More specific to the field of compulsive eating is the work of a number of researchers into the effects on behaviour of tryptophan and carbohydrate in the diet. Tryptophan, described as a natural relaxant, has aroused interest recently, because it has been described as a supplement to be taken for stress relief. It is an essential amino acid found in protein and requires vitamin B6 and magnesium for normal metabolism.

In fact, according to Peter Hudson, the body can often produce enough of its own tryptophan if sufficient vitamin B6 and magnesium are present – another very good reason for ensuring the complex carbohydrate content of the diet, i.e., eating enough whole grains in the form of brown rice, wholewheat bread and so on. It is particularly interesting to those looking at the link between food and behaviour because of its association with serotonin, which is involved in sleep and some aspects of mood. The amount of serotonin available to the brain depends on the amount of tryptophan taken up from the blood, which in turn depends on diet.

Because tryptophan must compete with the other amino acids for its place in the brain, a high protein meal creates too much competition and will not increase tryptophan. If you eat a meal of predominantly complex carbohydrates that also contains vitamin B6 and magnesium, the amount of tryptophan in the brain will be increased. Tryptophan also seems to help people who suffer from mild insomnia to fall asleep more quickly and this is obviously helpful to night eaters. Experiments suggest that even a moderate change in the daily diet, cutting out devitalized carbohydrates and substituting the natural, complex variety, could lead to a helpful alteration in behaviour with a lessening of stress.

Although these 'food in relation to behaviour' tests are still at an early stage they should not be dismissed lightly. If it turns out to be true that compulsive eaters could be helped towards controlling their disorder by re-balancing a biochemistry damaged by a junk food diet, a move towards fresh wholefoods would be not only advisable but essential.

Media pressures: food and diets

The fact that eating is a pleasant experience to the majority of people and that food has powerful psychological and emotional undertones, has been readily seized upon by the media. Food has become something of a new religion in our society. It is presented as a panacea for many human ills, and advertisers sell dreams along with the packages and cans. Anyone who questions this should sit by their television set during an entire evening and note how advertisements for food dominate the commercials. Apart from the innocent, informative advertisements that appear in some publications, almost all television commercials and a great many of the elaborate 'spreads' in national magazines and newspapers contain the absolute minimum of information. Their real aim is to work subtly on our feelings and semi-conscious attitudes by non-rational suggestions.

Take the commercial of the Dan Dare/Spiderman/Knight in Shining Armour character who risks every one of his nine lives to bring chocolates to his love – 'and all because the lady loves Milk Tray'. Or, consider that certain brand of nightcap that solves all the cares in the world. It becomes increasingly clear that the food or drink in each case has been used to suggest the key to some romantic, loving and comforting world, a dream that may be purchased along with the product.

The attitude of the media is to suggest that the all-important issue is not really what you *are* but what other people think of you. Your feelings, thoughts, body, your relationship with other people are all taken over, as it were, by this 'Big Brother' who tells you what you *should* buy, *should* do . . . *should eat*! There is an obvious relationship between this voice from without, and the disconnected, alien, inner part of yourself, that 'devil inside you', which dominates the life of the compulsive eater.

The media also suggests that, because 'everyone' enjoys a certain chocolate bar or ice cream, you are doing the right thing by eating it, because you are doing what other people do. It suggests that this is 'normal'. As the poet e. e. cummings described, the most difficult action is to remain yourself and that is a battle fought every day of your life. Never, in the world of the media, was the fight fiercer.

Maybe you are not the most confident person in the world. Many of the women we have talked to tell us that they feel unreal, a 'non-person'. They'll identify themselves as 'David's wife', 'Mrs Williams's daughter', or 'Karen's mother'. They buy food they do not really want to have in the house. They know it is the tempting variety of food they 'shouldn't have' but they buy it because the other members of the family demand it. They plan menus to please others, never themselves. It is, therefore, reassuring to have someone tell you that by buying such and such a confection you will be normal and 'in the swim'.

So you buy and eat, buy and eat. You disown your feelings. You are not important. Your personal control is gradually eroded, until you are brainwashed into believing that this or that food will satisfy much deeper needs than mere hunger or nutrition. It is not hunger that makes you crave these socially acceptable foods, you have developed the 'media appetite'. Karen never makes a shopping list. She decides on the food she will buy when she is in the supermarket, persuaded by the seductive illustrations on the packets of cakes, puddings and other sweet items. 'I seem to go into a kind of trance as I walk round the aisles,' she said. 'The "musak" soothes me and the food appears to hypnotize me so that I am always surprised by how much I have in the trolley when I reach the check-out point.' Unhappily for Karen and for many of us, in particular the potential or actual compulsive eater, sugary, starchy, processed foods are now considered desirable and these are the ones that feature largely in advertisements, lovingly depicted to the last photogenic calorie. There are plenty of commercials for chocolate, puddings and cakes but when was the last time you saw salads, fresh fruits or fish presented on the small screen as a 'status' product?

It is difficult to know how far the popularity of sweet things is due to palatability and how far to persuasion and conditioning. Almost without exception, human beings enjoy sweet things but the media has created a ritual out of buying and eating sweet things. In this saccharine world, we are led to believe that the key to showing your affection to others is food, that fatigue and depression, anxiety and stress, caused by everyday life in an often mundane world, can be easily relieved by stepping up your intake of sugary and starchy items, where the reward for unpleasant tasks is to 'treat yourself' to a sweet food because you 'deserve it' or even 'owe it to yourself'. The media's projected image of the good life, therefore, is notable for its emphasis on oral rather than spiritual comfort.

As for you, the compulsive eater, with your stresses and anxieties, your longing for a more satisfying, fulfilling life style and your fear, perhaps, of not being able to achieve it . . . how easy a prey you are for the media. Playing on these secret fears and wishes, it imprints on your mind the fact that food is the cure for everything and that you really 'need' those processed, refined carbohydrates, not only for energy but also for the power to succeed. Sophie loved the revived Ovaltine advertisement. 'It is the nostalgia that reaches me, reminding me of other, happier days. It certainly had a profound effect on me, recalling when I was a child. I disliked school and was always happy to escape at the end of the day. I would arrive home to a firelit, cosy room with the curtains drawn and my mother getting the tea. The table would be absolutely groaning with food: bread and butter, jam and cakes. I seemed to be accepting much more than food – more my mother's love, the security of home and of being a child. When I binge now, I find I go for these sorts of food.'

Food has a deep-seated role in society and plays its part in our emotional and social life. There are many situations in which food has a role that has nothing to do with nourishment or hunger.

Weddings are times when we eat sweet, delicious foods in order to join in the general happiness. Belief in a life hereafter allows the Irish to be joyful enough at a wake to make a hearty meal. Vance Packard, in his book *The Hidden Persuaders*, mentions a survey into the special meaning food has for people under stress or in hospital where they may be anxious about their health. He pointed out that, at such times, people prefer those foods that are well tried and liked.

What the advertiser does is to link insidiously his product with ideas and images which seem, on the surface, to be pleasurable, even commendable. Sexual love, femininity, maternal feelings are being constantly devalued by their association with food. It is as if these sentiments may be bought by rushing out to purchase chocolate, ice cream or pizzas. Mother-love seems to be the target most favoured and, as we have noted, the entangling of food and emotions is one sure way of launching children onto the road towards an eating disorder. Mothers are nudged into believing that they are failing in their role if they do not yield to Junior's plea for a proprietary brand of trifle. They are reassured that, by offering their children a chocolate bar between meals, this is a perfectly safe action because this sweet is 'different'. It will not ruin the appetite. They are told in psuedo-scientific terms that the youngsters need another form of confectionery in order to 'work, rest and play'. The media makes us more and more conscious of food out of the context of meal times, and undermines the will-power of the potentially compulsive eater until she believes she *should* be eating those refined carbohydrate-laden foods because they are 'nice' and because everyone else does. 'Oo!' says the cute little blonde in the cream cake advertisement. 'Naughty but nice!' And the viewer thinks if *she* can eat them and look like that, why shouldn't I?

The concern of the media is not to agonize about what is nutritionally good for us in the food it is trying to sell, but to find different angles in order to persuade us that, even if it is actually 'bad' for us, it is desirable. Guilt feelings about self-indulgence are assuaged by selling the sweets or chocolate in 'bite-sized' pieces, persuading the consumer that she does not have to eat it all, just a bite. Where the compulsive eater is concerned, we doubt it will stay at a bite.

Practically every food temptingly displayed on the

supermarket shelves contains sugar: the packages and mixes, the instant this and that, which the media has persuaded you you must buy, contain preservatives, including refined sugar. But this psychological drugging of the mind by the media's insistence on sweets and starches is only the beginning. Completely devoid of value because our bodies were never designed to metabolize such foods in large quantities, they must, inevitably, become a physical drug. As our systems become clogged with these huge amounts of potential energy we cannot use, everything goes haywire. The ever-appeased appetite turns into a biochemical craving for refined carbohydrates and the media has the compulsive eater effectively hooked. Often she will be someone with a very low tolerance of these carbohydrates, but the constant brainwashing by the media's commercials has developed her appetite for sugar and starch and her eating pattern is destined to become chaotic. From now on, just one piece of chocolate, just one slice of cheesecake can trigger off a binge.

But the media pressures on compulsive eaters are twofold: not only should they be eating sweet, convenience foods but – if they are women – they should be slim too. Slimming aids, new diets and slimming magazines occupy almost as much space as food advertisements. Patricia, a compulsive eater who also resorts to vomiting, told us that she feels she must have tried every diet in existence. And if she is not on a diet, she is always just about to embark on another 'miracle' regime. Women have a preoccupation with weight and dieting to keep slim. The 'right' shape seems to be more important as a means of sexual attraction for the female than for the male. This is one of several reasons why they are the likeliest victims of eating disorders. The media understands this female engrossment with 'thin is beautiful' and homes in on it. Magazines inculcate and suggest that the path to a specific, successful image lies in becoming slim. Their stories and features portray slender women in romantic settings and romantic relationships and the sexual impulses of women readers become channelled into a longing 'to be like that'.

Helen Gurley Brown, the American editor of *Cosmopolitan*, once said it was impossible to be too thin or too rich. The path to 'having it all' is through discipline and determination. Above all, says Gurley Brown, it is necessary to diet until you are as thin as a stick. She finds it impossible to imagine that any woman, determined to have it all, could wish to be fat, or even plump. Women who do not measure up she rates as 'mouseburgers'.

Lindy became a physical and mental wreck because of her conviction that she was such a mousey, worthless girl. Back in the 1960s, she worked alongside her sister, Twiggy, and another slender, equally blonde girl. 'I was not really overweight but they made me feel huge and fat by comparison,' she told us. 'It began to seem to me that you only had gorgeous boyfriends who whisked you off in white sports cars if you were very thin. It became an obsession and I began to diet, counting calories and starving myself until my nervous system suffered. Finally the strain became too great and I thought, "Damn it! I'll eat!" That was when I began to binge.' Lindy's experience, taken in context with the Gurley Brown statement, underlines how such an irresponsible attitude can be downright dangerous if read by those who are susceptible to eating disorders. How many, however, will take Gurley Brown's words seriously? Thousands! The power of the printed word is tremendous and so is the trust in those personalities that have been created by the media.

The magazine diets keep on coming: the grapefruit diet, the banana diet, the low fat, high protein diet and the exotic fruit diet. These are unbalanced, inadequate and ephemeral diets. The magazines must always have something new and bright to say. Next month they'll move on to the next 'can't fail' diet and so will you. The effect of such 'media diets' is to reduce people to a herd of sheep. No account is taken of the fact that each of us is an individual, that everyone's biochemical system is different and, thus, so must be our eating plan. It imbues women with an obsession with food as something they must deny themselves. It stereotypes food into 'good' and 'bad' categories. Dieters are brainwashed until food comes to assume emotive properties. Finally, they fear and cannot enjoy it . . . fertile ground for compulsive eating and other disorders!

Dieting can too easily become obsessive, creating stress and anxiety and making women worry increasingly about what to eat and how they look, until they rebel against these demands and eat 'something sweet' to make it up to themselves. There follows self-disgust and guilt – and possibly a binge.

'My grandmother was a model and was still working as one when I was a small child,' said Fiona. 'She impressed upon me that, unless I was really thin, I would never have a society wedding. My reaction was to stuff even more because I felt I could never measure up to that ideal.' Today's feminine shape is slim-hipped, neat-bosomed and wide-shouldered, an athletic young woman in the Raquel Welch mould. This 1980s version of the Venus di Milo smiles out at us from page three of the *Sun*, arousing admiration in men and envy and despair in women. In the past, art has helped to define the ideal woman. Nowadays, these ideas are largely presented not through art or religion but through the popular press, encouraging us to live in an unreal world.

The creation of this stereotype is subtle and costs a large amount of money. It has resulted in an enormous industry exploiting our destructive urge to diet. Young women are encouraged to develop the obsession that contributes to the selling of thousands of copies of magazines devoted to slimming. Over 250 million pounds are spent annually on slimming aids. Group therapy slimming clubs have sprung up, which not only over-emphasize the 'taboo' attitude towards certain foods but also increase the stress and strain of trying to lose weight by presenting women with unreasonable goals they cannot attain. It is surely not coincidental that many sufferers of bulimia whom we have seen have at some time joined such a club. They try to lose the required weight each week and when they fail, become desperate and guilty at having to face the other members whose approval or disapproval is verbally expressed. Stress and tension, as we have realized over and over again, provide an excellent launching pad for compulsive eating. Slimming clubs only perpetuate the pattern of weight loss and weight gain. According to statistics, 95 per cent of members regain the weight they lose and more.

The slimming industry enforces the belief that fat is ugly and that it is only the thin person who can enjoy the good life. It promises us that we can have our cake and eat it, too, by purchasing a calorie-reduced coke or soup, a slimmers' bread or biscuit. It promises us results without effort, lulling us further into that dream world where the only reality is the money chinking in the advertisers' pockets. Probably most serious is the fact that, while we may kid ourselves, we cannot kid our biochemical systems, which will react eventually, as they become unbalanced owing to improper nourishment.

One of our more startling letters came from a doctor who admitted her compulsive eating had been media-induced. 'I have had to come to terms with the fact that I now consider "thin is beautiful" and that my binge/starve pattern of eating is ruled by this. I do not know why I believe this. I am supposed to be an intelligent, rational person. But it has been drummed into me by what I read and view.'

The media slimmer's world is an 'if only' world – if only I were slim, if only I were thin enough to wear that bikini or those jeans, I could embark on a life style that would make me happy. Sooner or later, she realizes she cannot measure up to that ideal and turns to food as a relief. The magazine image of 'success' based on those dreams can only deepen the unhappiness and discontentment as we isolate ourselves from our bodies and deny ourselves permission to eat, but we still cannot reconcile the ideal shape in the magazine with our own.

One of the hardest steps for compulsive eaters seeking to find control is for them to accept themselves as they really are, plumpness and all. It is difficult for them to realize that their equation of thinness with success and happiness is an illusion. This acceptance of themselves as they truly are can go a long way towards breaking down the vicious circle of compulsive eating.

Angela possessed the slim, trim figure many of us would envy. She was tall, attractive and worked as a model. But when she came to the Centre she was on the verge of suicide because of her self-hatred about what she called her 'bulges'. Several months prior to this, she had found she was overweight and enlisted at one of the slimming clubs that seemed to have worked wonders for her friends. The first weeks had been a resounding success and the unwanted pounds dropped off. Then, one weekend, she found herself craving her favourite chocolate creams and, on impulse, she dashed out to buy a box. Angela ate the lot within a few minutes, finding she simply could not stop. Panic swept over her. When she returned to the club how would she explain the weight she had put on, and how would she face the boos of members when she admitted she had eaten a forbidden fruit?

That was how Angela's bulimia began and how she embarked on bingeing in the knowledge that she could rid herself of the unwanted food and not have to face up to the criticisms of others. She has not only risked her health but also her career. Bulimia has left its unpleasant trade mark of a bloated stomach.

If you have been accustomed to stuffing yourself with devitalized carbohydrates, such as white bread, refined sugars and cereals, cakes, pastries and chocolate, you will have to re-educate your tastes. You can develop a liking for any food, provided you eat only a little of it at first. Similarly, a wise mother can gradually introduce new foods into a child's diet, increasing the amount as he begins to enjoy it. Take the time to learn something about good nutrition, and enjoy those foods that are rich in vitamins and minerals and contain all the elements of a balanced diet. This can help to normalize your appetite and is far more important and effective than the media-induced panic to diet and lose weight.

Just as you can switch television channels, so you can plug into positive and negative thoughts. You can feel sorry for yourself and allow your thoughts to brood on the confectionery and creamy cakes you are denying yourself and, of course, fail and binge. Alternatively, you can feel calm and happy in the knowledge that you are tackling the problem with wisdom, reassuring yourself that there are foods that can be enjoyed and not feared.

The problem of being female

In writing this book, we discussed whether we should be accused of being sexist if we referred to compulsive eaters exclusively as 'she'. But we could not escape the fact that, of the people we have seen, the majority are women. In this section, we ask why it is that compulsive eating seems to be predominantly a female disorder and try to provide some of the reasons why.

'It's her hormones. She's moody, neurotic and hysterical.' These are familiar labels used to try to explain 'why', when the person who has a problem happens to be a woman. But is compulsive eating simply biologically determined? Certainly, from puberty, women experience a series of hormonal ups and downs with which they must cope and which are unparalleled in the lives of men. Men and women also differ under stress. Some researchers claim that women tend to have higher levels of adrenalin (related to fear) and lower levels of noradrenalin (related to anger) than men. This might help to explain the suggestion that women react to emotional conflict by developing a psychological disorder whereas men display physical symptoms.

The question of what is normal or average is hard enough without introducing gender stereotypes. Aggressive, 'manly' behaviour is not so acceptable in a woman. Similarly, the reason why more women are inclined to seek help with emotional problems and thus accept psychological help may be because it is more acceptable for them to admit to fears and phobias. We would suggest, therefore, that whereas women often have a hard time because of a hormonal imbalance, that is not the complete answer. Neither should women dismiss their eating problems as simply a 'question of hormones'. Pre-menstrual tension does exist but its severity relates to cultural attitudes and the traditional view taken of a woman's role. Where 'a woman's place is in the home', the woman is more likely to suffer from severe premenstrual symptoms. A change of focus can help many women enormously. If a woman is feeling irritable, longing to lash out, and then goes for a longed-for 'night out', the chances are her symptoms will decrease. Too often, women have long stretches of being on their own in the house and having time to brood. Symptoms grow out of all proportion – stress, tension, depression – and problems like compulsive eating begin. In common with eating disorders, premenstrual tension is a problem where the physical and psychological boundaries are blurred. When a woman begins to express herself; when she attributes worth to herself as an individual; and when her development is focused on herself rather than on other people, the symptoms, be they of premenstrual tension or of an eating disorder, tend to diminish. If it were merely a question of 'hormones' this would surely not be so.

In the case of the female compulsive eater, we suggest that, while part of her 'destiny' is biologically determined, a much greater influence comes from the conditioned behaviour of her sex in her particular social environment. In this section, we discuss Stavroulla in some detail because her story contains many elements of the conflicts that compulsive eaters face. Stavroulla is a young woman confronted by two differing cultures, that of her parents and that in which she now lives. She has already recognized that her salvation lies in self-expression, independence and escape from the very rigid gender role in which she has been placed.

It all begins very early. At the moment of birth, an entire chain reaction is set off depending on whether the baby is a boy or girl. Talking with many women in a society which treats men and women so differently, even the least liberated among them rebel. They sense the imbalance of power between men and women and are resentful. We suggest, therefore, that the female compulsive eater is not really 'sugar and spice and all things nice' but is more a constantly tamped down volcano that has to erupt.

Very early in our childhood girls are taught not to be violent or aggressive; they receive more sympathy if they cry for protection. Small boys are told it is weak to whimper and that they must stand up for themselves. But when the girl child becomes an adult and there is no one to listen to her cries, what does she do? Does she keep her mouth shut and sit on her clenched fists or does she repress her feelings of aggression, anger and hatred and turn to food?

Active ambition, self-assertion and forcefulness are seen as 'male' qualities. In conversation with some compulsive eaters they tell us they are unable to assert themselves, or put their own needs and personal values before those of others. They say 'yes' when what they really want to do is to shout an aggressive 'no!' 'No, I don't want to do that! No, I just don't feel like doing it now. No! It just isn't me!'

Louise is in her late thirties, unmarried, and looks after an elderly mother who suffers from ill health. Gradually, Louise has found her life reduced to the four walls of the house. Her mother is possessive and demanding – she has won the struggle for dominance over her daughter. Meals must be got on time and library books changed regularly. Louise sees her life as a hundred 'petty tasks'. She longs to rant and scream, she told us, and to beat her fists against the wall. 'It wouldn't be so bad if my brother took his share of the burden, but he says he cannot do so as he is married. And, after all, he tells me, he's a man. I'm the daughter of the house. This has

the effect of making me feel guilty about my anger and need
to rebel.' But no matter how guilty she feels, there is always
a residue of anger. It can be calmed by tranquillizers for a
while but it is never expressed and smoulders within Louise,
to erupt, eventually, into compulsive eating. Alone in the
kitchen while preparing her mother's meals, or in the middle
of the night, Louise stuffs, cramming food into her mouth
like an animal. She is a different woman altogether.

Women like Louise never say 'no'. They want to be
considered 'nice', 'good' and 'kind'. They wear masks. They
are blown like a weathercock this way and that, according to
the demands other people make on them. We meet them
every day: women who will alter an important appointment
to fit in with a husband; keep their day-to-day problems to
themselves; and put on a 'brave face', even altering their
voices to a tone they believe will please a lover or friend.

No wonder, like Jane, they have lost all sense of identity
except the wish to be 'normal', to be 'slim without having to
worry about it'. At least such an apparent goal is simple
compared with unearthing the real problem – discovering the
real Jane behind the smothering series of masks she has worn
throughout her life. As Madeleine told us: 'My mother
taught us that the "me" was the least important person in the
world. I should always put myself last and be polite and
tactful. She behaves that way herself and will do anything for
anyone.' Hannah, another compulsive eater, said: 'I am a
born crawler and would say black was white rather than
create a scene.' The aggressiveness is there, but because of
her conditioning a woman usually feels more anxious about
it and this inhibits her from expressing it. Even if she does,
she is more likely to be anxious afterwards than a man is.
Food, however, tranquillizes and blots out these 'taboo'
feelings.

Stavroulla uses food as a weapon against the emotions
aroused by her contentious upbringing. 'My parents were
Greek although I was brought up in England. My father's
attitude towards women has never really changed, which

means he lacks respect for them. As a result, I feel very inferior to men although intellectually I know this is false.' Just as her mother had been responsible for *her* younger brothers and sisters, so she has made Stavroulla responsible for hers. 'My relationship with her is much the same as her relationship with her mother except that, living in England, I have rebelled against her traditions. At a very young age, I did all the housework and had a lot of responsibility on my shoulders and yet, at the same time, I was not allowed to have any independence outside the family unit.'

Stavroulla remembers the anger and hate she felt towards her mother but if she showed any sign of her feelings she was beaten until she became quiet. Stavroulla longed to express her aggression but could not; and as this feeling was not, according to her parents, a 'womanly' feeling, she also experienced guilt. This was when her eating problem began. We have chosen to discuss Stavroulla at some length because, as a woman who was unable to express her anger, and who was not allowed any independence, she is a very good example of something that is almost universal among female compulsive eaters: that is a poor self-image; a lack of identity; obedience to the wishes of other people to the exclusion of her own; and the resorting to bingeing as a way of expressing inner feelings of aggression.

During one of the workshops at the Centre we asked a group of compulsive eaters to tell us of an occasion when in their eyes they were really horrible to someone. The actions they described seemed very minor. One woman described sending away a house decorator because he had arrived late and she had planned to go out; another refused to babysit for a neighbour, although she usually did so, and subsequently felt guilty about it all evening. The expressions they used to speak of their feelings seemed out of all proportion to the event: 'I felt awful about it.' 'I felt so very sorry afterwards.' 'I don't know what came over me.' These phrases, familiar to us, describe not only that part of themselves which they do not see as 'nice', 'kind' or 'feminine' but also an alien part of their personality they could not understand, the part they felt was responsible for their uncontrolled eating.

In this group, we discussed changing the word 'aggression' to 'self-assertion' and seeing this as a permissible way of expressing unfamiliar and strong emotions. These women could then acknowledge that they, too, had legitimate needs, which had sometimes to be put before those of others. The woman who had described her regret in sending away the decorator came to see that she had been justified in doing so because she had just as much 'right' as he did to follow through a planned programme. The other woman who had felt guilty about not babysitting realized that she had protected herself, defending herself from an unreasonably continuous demand. What had they done when they felt guilty about their so-called aggressiveness? They had binged. How did they feel now that they could rationalize their self-assertion? They felt in control of the situation, calm and satisfied.

Said Stavroulla: 'I feel there is a lot of suppressed energy inside me screaming to be released, like a volcano ready to erupt. Self-expression is my true purpose in life. I feel that marriage for me would happen only if I developed enough to become independent. I feel that to become closely attached to a man would produce a negative result as I become dependent far too quickly and my life revolves only around that person.' Stavroulla's fear is closely linked to her feelings of aggression.

The effect of marriage on men and women is very different. A woman is expected to make changes – her name, home, her job – and even if she continues to work it will be regarded as secondary to her 'real' role which is being a 'wife'. Increasingly, she must wear the mask of someone's wife or someone's mother as well as someone's employee. However well she copes, and some do extremely well, this woman of the 1980s may still wish to be 'feminine'; even the most liberated may still believe her husband's wishes should come before hers.

Sarah finds that escaping the house to do a part-time job helps her to control her eating, but having to return and prepare food for the family undoes that control. The loss of esteem and control that occurs in marriage must be responsible for that greater incidence of mental illness in women, particularly depression.

We suggested to another group of compulsive eaters that they imagine they were introducing themselves at a cocktail party. We told them they could be anything they wished – rich, famous, successful. During this exercise we found that most kept their own names, and although they were not married during their fantasizing, none had a very clear idea of her identity. Women, we suggest, are conditioned to lose a sense of personal worth and self-esteem through marriage and not to seek a strong self-image in order to ward off the anger that this frustration induces. The result is depression, a sense of powerlessness and lack of control as they turn their aggressive feelings in on themselves and the bingeing/guilt/depression/ bingeing syndrome begins.

Such an experience of marriage can have a very insidious effect, the feeling of helplessness and the eating disorder continuing long after the marriage is over. Jane suffers from bulimia and believed that if she were happier she would be able to give it up. But vomiting had become a way of life. 'I really don't know what my purpose in life is,' she told us. 'I was married for the first time when I was very young and gullible. I wasn't very pretty, was plump and short-sighted so I had to wear glasses. I looked up to my first husband and never dreamed he would be interested in me. When we were married and I had had my babies I thought I couldn't want anything more. But then I suppose I began to mature and I realized that he picked out my weak points and criticized me in order to make me feel inferior so that he could control me. I decided to improve my appearance and resorted to vomiting in order to reduce my weight. The ironical thing was that he finally left me for another rather plump girl. I'm happily married again but I cannot get over my fear of being out of control even though my second husband is very understanding. And I can't stop eating.'

Jean Baker Miller describes the task of wives as an 'endless job of emotional caretaking'. She says that the husband may come from any walk of life but the clearly defined job of the wife is always the same: to watch him for signs of stress, to understand him and give succour. The husband, however, will probably remain insensitive to *her* needs.

Madeleine resents this, and binges for 'comfort and reassurance'. She is an intelligent woman and has analysed the root of her own problem. 'I realize how narrow my life has become. I have allowed it to become that way. I have no time to myself because my husband is so possessive. But I know I must give myself time and space to develop.' For several weeks she planned to discuss this with her husband so that she could bring all her thoughts and feelings out into the open but he never 'has time' to listen.

If a wife becomes the bearer of the tensions and fears her husband brings in from the outside world, it is often because he not only demands it but also because she accepts the situation. The conflict remains unresolved and she retreats eventually into such disorders as compulsive eating.

Failure to come to terms with this loss of 'self' which a woman experiences through marriage can be likened to the failure of coming to terms with a bereavement. Comparative research has shown that while men react more aggressively to such a real loss, women are more apt to retreat into themselves. A woman's loss of identity remains unresolved and leads to feelings of worthlessness and low self-esteem. As one ex-journalist told us: 'I have no work satisfaction, no incentive to get anything done so I sit around and eat the moment the family isn't there.' When she worked on a busy newspaper there was no time to brood but now she has turned her once constructive, analytical power negatively onto herself. 'Why can't I be like other people and forget about "me"?' she asked us. 'I want to get on with living. I want to be good at what I do, whatever it is. I know I should get on my hind legs and do something positive instead of eating.'

With the increasing number of household machines, instant foods and swift cooking methods, together with the emphasis laid on women's fulfilment outside the home, housework has become less prestigious and seems to require fewer skills. Today, bread-making and cultivating the garden are not so much necessary as nostalgic quests to bring some significance into the lives of married women.

Trudy bakes bread once a week but it does not increase her sense of purpose and she resorts to cramming crusts and even uncooked dough into her mouth. She told us how she felt bloated after a binge and rushed out into the garden. 'I planted out all the bedding plants and for a while I felt more in control. But it didn't last long. The sense of being isolated, a nobody, even in the midst of my family, is hard to cope with.' Her conflict is encapsulated in another phrase: 'I love my husband. I know I've made his life hell with this problem. But I fight him constantly.'

One of the reasons why so much Valium and alcohol is consumed within such marriages is that they repress these outbursts. Here again, aggression and fear are often dealt with differently by men and women. It is still more socially acceptable for a man to go for 'Dutch courage', while women are more likely to demand drugs, such as tranquillizers and anti-depressants. Nevertheless, the number of women alcoholics is rising steeply: this is almost certainly a response to the same pressures that drive some women to drugs and others to eating. Whichever weapon is chosen to cope with the struggle its effect can only be to dampen down emotional responses and defeat any solution.

It reminds us of Delia who has come to the point of being able to say 'no' to her husband. Trevor was very ambitious and, wishing to bring off a deal, wanted Delia to attend a drinks session. She knew from bitter experience that drinking alcohol always set her off on a binge, but she felt she 'ought' to go to please him. The result was a massive eating session and that night she made a big decision. In future she would put herself first when her needs were as urgent as this. She agreed to attend these receptions but she would say politely and firmly that she preferred not to drink. Delia has shed some of the masks and is learning to listen to herself and to like what she hears. It is not always an easy path. It is far simpler to put it off and tell yourself that tomorrow you will wake up and the situation will have improved. Divorces are delayed every year because of this attitude, relationships are put into cold storage and eating problems are perpetuated.

The question of identity and self-worth has particular significance to the female compulsive eater and we suggest the following simple exercise. Examine your situation as it is now. Look ten years ahead and try to imagine how it will be if it continues unchanged. If you live now suffering from feelings of inferiority, low self-esteem, anger and guilt, how much more of a problem will this be in ten years' time when it will be a hundred times more difficult to change?

The carboholic

While this section attempts to offer reasons why someone may become a compulsive eater, we have to say that it remains a condition that frequently defies a simple explanation. No sooner have we pinpointed what appears to be *the* cause from the pattern which develops from the many cases we see, than along comes a case which contradicts it. This is inevitable in a disorder of which the symptoms cannot be labelled simply 'mental' or 'physical', but are more a mixture of disturbances in thought, feeling and behaviour. This is possibly why many general practitioners find it so difficult to treat.

The habit of prescribing drugs to compulsive eaters – slimming pills, anti-depressants, sedatives – can only upset the balance of a body already threatened by impoverished foods and bad eating habits. Balance is essential in the body mechanism to keep the on/off satiety switches working efficiently; it is especially so in cases where the cause may well be physical and may depend on how an individual copes with the food she eats.

Because we are not medically trained we cannot prove this with laboratory testing. But we are convinced from the sufferers' accounts that the idea of hypersensitivity to food provides one key to some cases of compulsive eating.

Everyone is different and so is our tolerance to our physical and social environment. Our bodies are constantly adapting to physical and mental strains. Let us take something as basic as a loud noise: your reaction will be very different from that of your slightly deaf great-uncle. And when it comes to food, 'one man's meat is another man's poison' contains more truth than we probably realize. *Our* response will be entirely different from *theirs* and will depend on several things: the amount we eat, what we eat, how often we eat it, and just how intolerant we are to that food. Hugely swollen lips after just a mouthful of crab or lobster or a 'strawberry' rash – that is the image most of us have of food allergy. And we find it easy to accept someone's almost instantaneous adverse reaction to food they do not usually eat.

But what we are suggesting is that there are far more insidious processes going on within the body that result in a condition which compulsive eaters describe in many ways: 'getting used to food'; 'getting the taste for food'; 'having cravings – particularly carbohydrate cravings'; or 'needing something sweet'. For the purposes of this section, we call it food addiction. We suggest that a food you enjoy and eat every day, be it bread, chocolate, eggs or breakfast cereal, might not only be making you feel depressed and unreasonably fatigued but could also be the reason why you have found yourself eating compulsively. Although there is no immediate cause and effect response, this hypersensitivity to a particular food is, in fact, far more common than the more dramatic and obvious allergy. It is more subtle, too, because it can lead to a dependency, akin to that of alcoholism.

The notion of intolerance to certain foods is old and appears in the writings of Hippocrates. Although such an intolerance does not produce the antibodies of a 'classic' allergy, such as pollen-caused hay fever, the first self-healing process is much the same: the body musters its forces in an attempt to adapt itself to this foreign agent. That is why hypersensitivity to food often remains secret a long time and is hard to track down. You actually feel better after you have eaten that bread or chocolate, as the alcoholic feels better after those first drinks. The unpleasant symptoms, the depression and fatigue, above all the craving to eat and eat and carry on eating, can be staved off, at least for a while.

Zoe has 'always' eaten dried fruit. She realized that her binges had to include something that contained it, a Christmas pudding or two, muesli or mince-pies. Vera could not let a day pass without gorging on Mars bars. Each of them, compulsively and continuously, ate substances to which they were intolerant, but which soothed them at the time. Although, in fact, they were becoming less tolerant to these foods, their bodies had 'learnt' that, as long as they kept themselves on a maintenance dose, the symptoms could be delayed. The key is timing: with a classic allergy, the swelling and the rash happen immediately; with a hidden food intolerance, the symptoms are prolonged. This way you never suspect that the refined carbohydrate you crave could be the 'rogue food'.

Thanks to Hans Selye who has made its study his life's work, the word 'stress' has been given a new and wider meaning – that of any outside agent which causes wear and tear to the body organism. When the body comes under siege and is alerted, it begins to build up a resistance by producing increased quantities of the 'stress hormones'. What is crucial is the individual response: not what happens so much as the way you react to it. Sooner or later, the ability to adapt is exhausted, the 'chemist shop' closes down and the body succumbs.

The same drama is played out when it is a food that is intolerable to an individual: initial alarm and then adaptation, which could well explain your 'hunger' to the point of craving certain foods, often sugar and refined carbohydrate based. Whenever you begin to feel 'down' you resort to bingeing and as time goes by the binges become more frequent, may increase in quantity and be centred around the substance that seems to 'pick you up' and keep you going. This can last a long time as you continue to eat indiscriminately and in large, often grotesque, quantities, unconsciously searching for the secret substance that your body has learnt to crave. Discovering hypersensitivity to certain foods can well be the key that frees some prisoners from the secret cage. It also gives a physiological basis to the concept of *them* and *us*. We all know those 'lucky people' who can eat a little of what they fancy, whenever they fancy it and never crave it.

Patricia came to the Centre because of her anxiety over the increase of her feasting and fasting. She looked full of life and health but explained that she 'woke up tired'. It was not a normal fatigue, she told us, but was associated with feelings of nervousness for no apparent reason, tension and frustration. Patricia was asked to keep a food chart on which she recorded every crumb of food that passed her lips over a period of time. The item that featured constantly was processed breakfast cereals. Patricia ate them every morning without fail and often had some at lunchtime. If she wanted an evening snack it was, inevitably, cereals. 'But I love my cereals!' she protested when we suggested she experiment and cut them out of her diet for a week or so. She was willing to co-operate, however, and soon saw for herself that the moment her cereal intake had been reduced, her strange fatigue and hunger began to disappear.

There was a postscript. A few weeks ago, Patricia arrived at the Centre looking awful. 'I thought a bowl of cereals wouldn't hurt now and again,' she said, 'but you were right.

It started off an enormous binge. I shan't try to prove you wrong again.'

Intolerance or hypersensitivity to certain foods might also explain some cases of night eating. Compulsive eaters know all too well that panicky feeling should they wake up between three and five in the morning, with the 'night terrors' as one sufferer put it. A raid on the refrigerator will be much more effective than a sleeping pill. Night eating, which has always seemed such a mystery, begins to make sense when you realize that your body is busily adapting to a food to which it is intolerant, and that this is the longest period in the twenty-four hours when you go without your 'fix' and you could experience withdrawal symptoms or cravings, which wake you up.

Another reason why you may begin to experience these 'hungover' feelings is because of the eating pattern or 'chaos' of the compulsive eater. Suppose you are hypersensitive to processed flour and have gorged on bread. During the subsequent 'fast' you could well begin to realize the extent of your withdrawal symptoms, how near you are to addiction and how the uneasy craving can only be soothed by taking more of the same stuff. The vicious circle is created once more: you binge until you are addicted to certain foods, you then try to avoid them and develop withdrawal symptoms that naturally produce cravings for these same foods. Olivia knows that feeling. She keeps a stock of biscuits and chocolates by her bed, in order to relieve that sinking feeling during the night.

Night eating, if you are a food-intolerant, compulsive eater, heralds the onset of the third stage: addiction. It can be as painful and acute as any other form of addiction, the difference being that you probably do not know what you are craving and subconsciously search for it during your binges. In their book *Allergies: Your Hidden Enemy*, the authors, Drs Theron G. Randolph and Ralph W. Moss, quote the case of an overweight, middle-aged woman who had been admitted to hospital for treatment of depression after two attempted suicides. She said she had reached the point where once she began to eat she felt as if she simply could not stop. Her favourite food was peanut butter which she said was the one indispensable item. She also loved bread and anything made from wheat. After tests, she avoided these foods which were proven not to agree with her and saw a remarkable diminishing both of her depression and her eating disorder.

As your addiction progresses and the withdrawal symptoms increase, depression may come to dominate your life. And although we suggest that there is a possible physical origin to your eating disorder, that you may be able to 'switch off' by cutting out certain foods, we are not under-estimating the real and crippling nature of this depression.

A varied diet is important to us all but particularly so to a person whose body is inclined towards food intolerance. In fact, it can actually create new cravings if the same foods are eaten too often. To judge by their food charts, many compulsive eaters have a monotonous diet.

Although we underline that the food-intolerant, compulsive eater's problem is a result of the body influencing the behaviour of the mind and not the other way about, emotional upsets can certainly tip your tendency to hypersensitivity over to the third stage of addiction. This is likely because emotional stress will exhaust further your protective hormones and lower your defences. Day in and day out, your body struggles to remain normal in the face of many physical and psychological stresses, from noisy cities to imperfect food. Stress can trigger off many diseases. It will affect *us* differently from *them*. That is why the compulsive eater is not 'weak-willed' as some people believe. That is why we listen to and do not dismiss as an 'excuse for eating' the conviction of such people that they are 'addicted' to food and crave carbohydrates, to the extent of being 'carboholics'.

Under stress, *they* lose their appetite. For *us* it is a signal for a strong desire to eat and assuage those feelings of anger, guilt, depression and tension. The compulsive eater, who can 'get no satisfaction', continues to eat and eat, not relishing the food but determined to consume large quantities. Periods of fasting on a health farm can put her into an agonizing state of withdrawal. The short story of the desperately hungry inmates of a health hydro who went stealthily to the village for sausage rolls and other 'taboo' foods must have struck a chord in many compulsive eaters. Deprivation for them leads to bingeing and the habit of turning to carbohydrates for consolation in times of anxiety, depression and stress can only cause more metabolic chaos.

That is one of the reasons why we never advocate such dieting for compulsive eaters, and why an eating plan that features frequent, small meals and is full of fresh wholefoods, absent in refined carbohydrates, will keep things running more smoothly. It seems to be these devitalized carbohydrates that 'throw the switch', confusing our systems over their feelings of hunger or satiety.

This comparison with an overload in an electrical system is one way of explaining the breakdown in the 'I've had enough' mechanism. In terms of evolution, the sudden introduction of refined, processed carbohydrates into our diets in such large quantities may well have created a dysfunction of the 'reward system' in some people which leads to a craving for more of the same items. However, the sensation described by many sufferers of feeling hungry twenty minutes after a large meal can also be caused, sometimes, simply by eating too quickly. It is not always our 'fault' that we have thrown the mechanism. Manufacturers add sugar to just about everything and refine and process many daily items so that it is very difficult to monitor our intake of these substances.

If you manage to discover that there is a certain food which appears to trigger off a binge, your only solution is to cut it out altogether. In the course of our work on this book we have noticed that chocolate, refined sugars and starches feature largely on the list of 'triggers'. Muesli is another saboteur. Because it is reputed to be a 'healthy' food, sufferers do not realize that it might also be responsible, in their cases, for some very unhealthy eating habits. Refined flour is another culprit. Whatever the 'poison' for the taker of drugs, the alcoholic or the carboholic, the pattern of dependency is the same. It moves from increasing the amount to the person's life becoming centred upon getting and consuming the substance. For compulsive eaters, the time spent eating food increases at the expense of all other activities and the maintenance of a supply of food becomes *the* necessity.

There is, however, a unique problem with food addiction and that is you cannot exist without eating. An alcoholic can stop drinking completely. A smoker can give up cigarettes. But a food addict cannot give up food. What she can do is to discover what foods act as triggers to her particular addiction and avoid them completely. Discovering your particular food intolerance may be difficult. Check to see if a significant or excessive use of any one item of food is cropping up in your diet more than once in three days, and also beware if you find you are beginning to eat what you consider to be a 'safe' food in increasing quantities. You could develop a sensitivity to it and become addicted. This will soon become apparent. Experiment with new dishes. Eat natural foods in a plain and simple form and cut out the packages and mixes that creep into so many of our diets. Give your body a 'rest' by rotating foods. If, for example, you eat wheat one day, go without it for several days, before eating it again. This way you put less strain on your system. Following a regime like this could be the answer for a carboholic.

Coming to terms with your shape

Compulsive eaters are always willing to grasp at anything that might help the disorder. They are forever seeking a logical reason for such illogical behaviour, longing for someone to wave a nutritional magic wand and set them free. We've already found that there are many answers to the question, 'Why do I eat compulsively?' They are loneliness, boredom, frustration, non-communication, childhood over-indulgence, under-indulgence, or even a subconscious fear of physical attractiveness.

One new explanation has been put forward in a recently published book, *The Dieter's Dilemma*, by William Bennett and Joel Gurin. This is the 'set point' theory. At first sight, this seems to be such a magic wand because it waves away all question of responsibility, and lays the blame for failed dieting fairly and squarely on a mechanism outside your control. It tells you that if you are not skinny or slim it is simply because you were not 'meant' to be so. In their book, Bennett and Gurin suggest that each of us has a 'set point' weight, around which our bodies naturally hover. They liken this 'set point' mechanism to a thermostat and describe how, at times of weight loss or gain, particularly during periods of dieting, this 'set point' mechanism urges a change in our behaviour so that we can re-establish our set body weight.

The dieter experiences a gnawing pressure to eat more. Even if she resists and continues to deprive herself, this feeling develops into an uncontrollable hunger while her early restlessness slackens as her body tries to conserve energy. Long-term dieters, they say, may live under permanent stress from these internal signals, which can only be relieved by binges that help the body to return to its destined fat level. When we read the book it seemed to us to give a precise description of the process of compulsive eating and accounted neatly for the fast/feast pattern and the trial both of body and mind that compulsive eaters experience when they deprive themselves. But we don't feel that the 'set point' theory explains properly all the aspects of compulsive eating. It is true that many people are aware of a typical weight around which they hover, never going much below it without a struggle and finding it easier to rise above it. But for the compulsive eater, there are many other factors that trigger off her eating – media pressures, childhood difficulties, food addictions – which seem to make the story much more complex. Numerous studies on rats have looked at the way in which the body attempts to control appetite, eating habits and weight. But we would like to point out that compulsive eaters are not laboratory animals. Rats do not watch seductive television commercials convincing themselves that a confectionery may be nice, if naughty; they do not have relationship problems from babyhood to adolescence, nor do they feel ashamed of their body image or afraid of sex. As far as we know they communicate sufficiently for their needs; and there are no male and female stereotypes in the world of the rat, neither are there junk foods nor tranquillizers. Rats may overeat under certain conditions, specifically under stress.

Hetty Einzig, co-author with Geoffrey Cannon of *Dieting Makes You Fat*, writing in *Successful Slimming* magazine, described women's conflict between their two roles: the plump 'mother' stereotype and that of the skinny 'superwoman'. She believes that both are too limiting and suggests that a woman can discover the strength and power of her individual physical self by a balance of exercise and nutrition. We also believe that we must abandon the unrealistic aspiration to extreme slimness, which characterizes the thinking of too many women. We should look this skinny, immature image in the face and decide to banish it from our minds, and find instead the best shape and size for ourselves as individuals, within reasonable limits. We should ask ourselves why we *have* to be a certain weight particularly if it is an unrealistic one for us. The magic of numbers rules the weight-watcher's life – just under the 8-stone mark being a potent one, to judge by what our compulsive eaters tell us. Why? Pauline supplied the answer. 'I *had* to be 7 stone 12 pounds and I became panicky if I crept up above that weight. I was desperate not to weigh 9 stone because if I was just under 8 stone, it gave me leeway to binge. It was rather like knowing you have some money in your account which you can draw on. The strange thing is that now I have accepted that 9 stone is probably a reasonable weight for me, I don't binge.'

We have liberated ourselves in sexual matters, it seems, only to find a new form of guilt and disgust in food. The new 'religion' appears to be that fatness leads to hell and slimness, by strict dieting, takes us to paradise. We still have some growing up to do. We need to be aware of our bodies. With time, and it will take time, we can adapt those bodies to new eating habits that will have nothing in common with fad diets, and we can attain and hold our optimum weight when it is based on a much wider-ranging and realistic graph than that found in many women's magazines. Happily, there are already signs of this coming of age in our society. A short while ago, many of us became miserable and diet-mad because we felt we could not fit into the fashionably skinny body image. One of the writers remembers the unrealistic weight chart in a national magazine that set her onto a panic-diet regime, ending in anorexia nervosa. Today, the desirable shape is curvaceous, a far cry from the characterless, 1960s' waif. Today's beauties are more dynamic, the dumb blonde image is dated. It is shape more than weight that matters and the new generation of 'exercise goddesses', even if they demand we undergo the Fonda 'burn', are a healthy sign of this.

We believe that 'getting into shape' rather than 'losing weight' is a much more positive goal. Every one of us was born with a natural pattern of behaviour to support our bodily needs. As a baby you ate when you were hungry as much as you needed and when you were blissfully satisfied, you stopped. Then outside influences began to interfere. As adults we unlearn this natural habit and constant dieting confuses our bodies even more. If you can learn to trust and respect your system again, and learn to listen to it, you will know, deep down, what is right for you. Compulsive eaters *do* have this ability. Their systems *are* sensitive. But they have smothered that sensitivity to food, overtaxed their digestive apparatus and baffled their metabolism. This food overload sedates their responses until they become out of control and the brain's appestat switch is thrown. Dieting for the compulsive eater is not only a reaction against putting on weight, it is also a guilty reaction to overeating. The goal is not achieved by calorie-counting but by tuning into the natural mind and body processes again.

Many things make people eat compulsively. There is a part of the brain which, as a rule, helps you to balance the food you eat with the food you need. If you become over-anxious, if there is a hormonal imbalance or if you are addicted to certain foods, the sensitive setting of your appestat can be upset. 'Set point' disciples use their theory to explain hunger. It explains why certain people who have a very low 'set point' do not yearn for calories and those who have a high 'set point' constantly struggle against hunger whenever they attempt to be slimmer than their body's chemistry dictates. We suggest that this hunger which strikes dieters could also be due to dysnutrition. In our society a huge quantity of food is available, but quality is lacking in many of our eating plans.

Take the case of Diana. Her food-intake chart revealed that she exists on a diet dominated by 'giant cookies', chocolate, pasta, biscuits, coffee and buttered scones. There is a serious lack of balanced nutrients and we found it amazing that she, in common with many of the highly educated young women we see, has a very hazy idea of nutrition. 'Protein's in bran, isn't it?' she suggested, brightly.

A glance at Diana's food-intake chart showed us that she is not only ignorant of good nutrition but also very deficient in many important nutrients. We have already discussed those food cravings which come about as the result of a growing addiction to a specific item or to refined and processed carbohydrates but these wild panics for food can often be nature's way of telling us that we are getting insufficient vitamins and minerals, our bodies' 'sparking plugs'.

The word protein comes from a Greek word meaning 'to come first'. When protein foods are under-supplied, the body tissues fail to be repaired normally and because muscle is made up of protein, a lack of this invaluable substance eventually results in muscles that are soft and stringy, which means flabbiness and poor posture. If you eat an unbalanced diet over a period of time, you can actually begin to look different: your facial muscles will be inclined to droop, your body will look flabbier and fatter, although you may have lost weight. It is the elastic pull of healthy muscles which keeps the contours firm and youthful. You also need carbohydrates, of course, of the unrefined, complex variety. If too few of these are eaten to supply the energy needs of your body, it will begin to burn up proteins for this purpose, although they might be needed for the jobs of building and repair. Proteins, too, cannot be broken down completely and the remaining waste products are excreted from the blood stream through the kidneys. Although a diet containing adequate proteins is essential, excessive intake of them may be harmful. The high protein, low carbohydrate diet is a regime that originated in America but more recent research has shown that one with a high percentage of complex, unrefined carbohydrates and fresh, uncooked foods has a lot in its favour. A diet like this, combined with regular exercise, seems to be the ideal way of living for people with eating disorders.

The problem with a low calorie diet for compulsive eaters is that the body is marvellously adaptable and will do anything to preserve its essential functions. After a few weeks' practice, it adjusts to a lower metabolic rate, slowing down the furnace and becoming mean with its fuel in order to get the most out of available energy. You can now run on as little as 1000 calories a day without further weight loss and may lose only a little weight on 800 calories. Exercise is the only way of climbing out of the metabolic rut. But, as the 'set point' theory tells us, exercise is not just a matter of burning up more calories in a simple adjustment to the input/output equation. The metabolism seems to be affected, overall, by exercise. With exercise, an active body is automatically more geared to be leaner than is an inactive one.

There are many reasons why exercise 'works'. It stops you 'thinking food'. Fad diets concentrate your attention on what you eat or do not eat, when you eat and when you can eat again. They convince you that if you do your calorie sums correctly you will lose weight. If you go over your calorie total, disaster will strike. Exercise makes you look good. Over a period of time and done at regular intervals your skin and hair condition will improve with the increased blood flow. Exercise tones up your muscles and gives you shape. It makes you feel good because its effect is to improve your energy quota, tone up the digestive functions and help you to sleep better. The deep breathing required when doing endurance or aerobic exercises relaxes you and combats stress and tension by using up those 'fight or flight' chemicals which may be in our blood stream. Outlets for alleviating stress in our society are limited – a regular exercise programme is one outlet – and stress is one of the major triggers to eating compulsively. Exercise helps you to feel more confident and to develop a better self-image. As Hetty Einzig has described in her book, it liberates women physically and they discover the power they have over their own bodies.

Compulsive eaters need exercise even more than *them*. Often, *they* seem to possess bodies that can control accurately the input/output balance. *We* are not so good at it. For one or more reasons, there is an imbalance in *our* bodies but we can achieve that balance again.

Stella told us: 'I had dieted on and off for years, longing to be thin, but always put the weight back on in weeks or months. Finally, I decided to trust my own body. I had no target weight, no diet, nor a particular goal as to how slim I should be. I just told myself that, in time, my body would be slimmer and fitter. I took up running and cut out all refined foods. My attitude towards food has completely changed. I can eat now without worrying whether I will have enough self-control to stop myself, and I am not always counting calories. I can leave food on my plate – something that was unthinkable in the past. I actually like my body and have confidence in my control of it. I know I'll never binge and starve again.'

How your faulty appestat control came about is uncertain – nature or nurture, mind or body influences. It is important, however, to know that you are not doomed to a perpetual fast/feast treadmill. The 'set point' theory reminds us that the best shape for each of us may be the body we have toned and made energy-efficient by exercise.

Low blood sugar

'I wish I could stop thinking about food and eating' is the complaint of every compulsive eater. In this chapter we have looked at some of the different reasons why compulsive eaters may have climbed onto that destructive merry-go-round. These include personal histories, early habits of eating or of deprivation, outside social influences, a sense of inferiority, food intolerance or an unrealistic body image. We have continually underlined the fact that each individual responds differently to these stresses, and that stresses, which might not have much effect on *them*, obviously have a marked one on *us*.

In this final section we look at one explanation for compulsive eating which seems very important to us: low blood sugar. The 'sugar blues' or hypoglycaemia, as chemically low blood sugar levels in the body is called, has become the fashionable complaint, an umbrella diagnosis for the many vague and indefinable symptoms that beset us these days. It has been held responsible for depression, irritability, headaches, weakness and a number of the symptoms which may urge us to eat. It is understandable, therefore, that the compulsive eater should jump onto that bandwagon. A low blood sugar level could explain the mystery of an unnatural hunger and give the habit of compulsive eating a respectable name.

It is a fact, however, that many of the compulsive eaters we see *do* have very unstable blood sugar levels but not to the extent where it would be clinically diagnosed as such. Many of them have no energy, possessing symptoms typical of hypoglycaemia, such as dizziness, headaches and an amazing hunger. We are not doctors, as we have stressed elsewhere, but we have watched symptoms disappear when compulsive eaters followed an adequately balanced eating plan.

Fluctuating blood sugar levels happen to all of us. When they are up you feel good and you do not want to eat. When the level drops, you feel tired and irritable. You cannot concentrate and you crave 'something sweet'. Why do you think so many family rows take place before breakfast or supper? People who need to eat to normalize their blood sugar level do not feel well until they do so.

Your brain is the conductor of your body's orchestrated organs. It functions on glucose (or sugar), so the maintenance of that sugar at a certain level is important as brain fuel. Cells in your pancreas monitor these blood sugar levels all the time and release insulin accordingly. If you have a meal which sends your sugar level up, the insulin production rises. This hormone makes the body cells receptive to the storage of fuel, removing excess sugar from the blood stream so as to bring the levels back to normal. When your body is in the 'hungry state' and the circulating sugar begins to decrease, low levels of insulin draw the fuel out of storage in an attempt to keep the sugar level up. You feel lethargic as the blood sugar is used up and, as it falls, you begin to crave 'something sweet'. If it drops even lower it will bring on exhaustion, a bad headache, weakness and lack of concentration.

Sometimes the process does not work as it should and then a condition of hypoglycaemia may be diagnosed. If you suspect this you would be sensible to have a six-hour glucose tolerance test by your doctor. Some people, without such a test and assuming they have chemical hypoglycaemia, have put themselves on a regime of high protein and no refined carbohydrates, only to find they have more symptoms, not fewer. Their problem was an insufficiency of everything, including those valuable complex carbohydrates. However, the type of fuel you use to stoke your body does affect blood sugar levels. If your choice is high in protein, this will result in a slow increase in blood sugar, lasting about four hours, during which time you will not feel so inclined to nibble. If, on the other hand, you pack in refined carbohydrates, the level shoots up and there is a short-lived feeling of well-being, followed by a steep drop when you crave 'something sweet'. The effect of eating fat is halfway between that of protein and carbohydrate.

A glance at Diana's food chart shows that sweet pastries and sugary foods figure largely on it. Their effect makes her feel fine temporarily, but within two hours she is weak and hungry. Diana tops up with more chocolate and more biscuits when what she really needs is a proper food balance. Being a compulsive eater, however, she is accustomed to feeling low and does not recognize this need. An eating pattern on these lines sends the blood sugar soaring swiftly. It stimulates the pancreas to pour out insulin and this causes Diana to feel hungry. The excess glucose will eventually end up as fat. Diana's next so-called meal is sugar-packed so the message goes back to the pancreas: 'send up more insulin'. Her system overworks. The sugar is withdrawn because of the over-supply of insulin and instead of those chocolate bars giving her vitality she begins to feel very tired. If, like Diana, you continue to eat this sort of food, your blood sugar levels behave like a yo yo, shooting up and down far too rapidly. Increasingly, you will have the same sensations as if you had not eaten: abnormal hunger and fatigue.

If Diana ate a meal of, say, fish, a green salad, wholemeal bread and some fruit, she would have far more zest and even lose her craving for sweet things. Such a meal is digested more slowly. The sugars from the fruit have to be released from the plant cells and the starch from the bread has to be broken down to glucose (a simple sugar) before being absorbed into the blood stream. This staggered absorption of glucose avoids not only an excessively high jump in the blood sugar level but also an excessive production of insulin to counteract it. High levels of insulin cause hunger.

Like many people, we used to read about these processes, found them interesting, but firmly believed they applied to other people, never to us. We know differently, now. Diana was adamant that she ate chocolate when she felt dizzy because it made her feel better. She would not believe that she was creating a destructive, vicious circle. A few weeks ago, she came to us, still incredulous. 'I feel so well. I've eaten the way you suggested and I've got all this energy from somewhere.'

We spent a long time with Diana going through the principles of a proper eating plan that cut out all the devitalized, refined sugars and carbohydrates, eliminated caffeine and decreased the number of cigarettes and alcohol, while concentrating on fresh wholefood. We were excited when we received her proposed shopping list. A reformed person! It was only when we reached the last page that our hearts sank. Diana had listed all the 'treats': the chocolate and biscuits, the 'fun-sized' sweets and sugary snacks she felt she could 'allow' herself for having stuck to the eating plan designed to help her low-ish blood sugar levels. Frequently, we have to tell intelligent girls like Diana that they are suffering from malnutrition – they eat sugar at the expense of everything else. 'Something sweet' was Diana's idea of a treat. We asked her: 'Can't you give yourself a treat that is not food? Buy a book, some new nail varnish or go to the hairdressers.' She looked shamefaced. 'Oh, yes, I never thought of that.'

This sugar addiction is likely to start with the very young. In Great Britain, the average child obtains between 25 per cent and 35 per cent of its total calories from sugar. Even breast milk is very sweet (perhaps the source of our fondness for sugar), and many baby foods, which claim a correct dietary balance, contain refined sugar. It is as well to take a closer look at the small print. Even if we want to escape sugar it is very difficult these days to do so. The media tells us we need it to 'work, rest and play'. Our national consumption of sugar is on the increase.

While children are tiny it is relatively easy to train them not to enjoy 'neat' sugar, giving them an apple or a piece of carrot instead of a chocolate bar. But as Penelope Leach points out, it is foolish to try to ban all sweets from a child's diet. It is better, she says, to select the sweets, choosing varieties that are not so likely to 'cling' to the teeth, and give the children a ration, which they eat at a set time. They should then clean their teeth. When they start primary school and spend more time with other children, 'sweet trouble', as Penelope Leach calls it, may begin. Mothers have our sympathy here. Even if they are firm and manage to cut out almost all sugar from the family's diet, they cannot be on guard against schoolfriends and relations all the time feeding them 'treats'. Far better to allow a sweet 'ration' and thus diminish the role of sweets so that they represent only a part of life's bounties, rather than create a forbidden fruit that only becomes more desirable and craved after, and to be eaten in secret.

Sugar has come into our lives as a huge, advancing avalanche. Other changes in our diet have come about over hundreds of years. It is only in the last two hundred years that we have been subjected to these enormous amounts of refined sugar. One problem is that, in its concentrated form, we can consume amounts far greater than we can in its natural form. Such sugar satisfies our appetites while offering no nutrients; it simply presents our bodies with a substance they cannot use. In a more natural environment we would find sugar in unrefined cereals or fruit and our normal capacity would not allow us to eat more than a limited amount. Some of us, it seems, can cope with this influx better than others. For compulsive eaters too much sugar means cravings and a binge.

Anyone who suffers from an eating disorder and wishes to find control should be aware of what good nutrition means and how sugar has no part in it. When we see the irritability and depression that can be brought about by low blood sugar levels in diets high in refined sugar, we realize that it is 'dangerous' in more ways than one. You do not need the sugar you sprinkle on that starchy processed cereal or slip into your tea or coffee. You are far better off without the 'hidden sugar' in that glass of cola, piece of cake, pie, ice cream or pudding. When you think that there is the equivalent of two teaspoonfuls of sugar in one biscuit, imagine how much may be taken on a binge! Your brain and nervous system do need a very small amount of glucose to function, but this can be more safely obtained from fruits, vegetables or unrefined starchy foods that are gradually broken down before passing into the blood stream as glucose.

Fruits, vegetables and milk contain sugars. Sucrose (common table sugar) is found in sugar beet, sugar cane, maple syrup and dates. Glucose (grape sugar) is found in grapes and in honey. Fructose (fruit sugar) is found in most fruits and lactose (milk sugar) in milk. There are numerous other less important sugars but all are recognizable from food labels as they end in *ose*, and they normally end up as glucose in the blood stream. Many vegetables and all cereals contain starches which are split up into glucose. There is no danger of going short of glucose for the brain! The danger is in overeating sugars and starches, which stimulate excessive hunger, and lead to more overeating and eventually to getting fat.

Many compulsive eaters deal with stress by eating the wrong foods, skipping meals and bingeing on sugar items. Some of them seem to go for days on little more than black coffee and cigarettes – and then go on a binge. Coffee, drugs, alcohol and cigarettes can all have a direct effect on blood sugar levels. First, they stimulate the production of the adrenal hormone which increases the blood sugar to produce the familiar 'lift' we feel we need at times of stress. Insulin quickly comes into action and causes the sugar level to fall again. This effect explains the coffee addict's or chain smoker's problem of continually craving yet another pick-up. 'Highs' and 'lows' of mood come to light on many food charts. We asked how they felt after they had eaten. Did they have any symptoms of stress or fatigue? Did they experience cold sweats, hot sweats, shakes, headaches, palpitations or dizziness? Anxious about these inexplicable sensations, many compulsive eaters take a tranquilliser, smoke a cigarette or turn to 'something sweet' and succeed only in creating a further imbalance. The effect of alcohol is not dissimilar. Like 'neat' sugar, it picks you up then brings you down until a regular pattern of craving is formed. Many 'cured' alcoholics substitute sweets for alcohol and this underlines the relationship between the two.

Some people are more prone to unstable blood sugar levels. Some nutrients affect blood sugar levels. A third source of the problem is hormonal. For the female compulsive eater, therefore, the pre-menstrual syndrome is especially important. In fact, it is true to say that almost all the women with eating disorders whom we have seen, experience an increased difficulty in controlling their eating during this time of the month. It is evident from their food-intake charts: while they find it easier to eat sensibly and at fairly regular intervals during the rest of the month, they have had marked cravings in the pre-menstrual days. As Eve told us: 'It's never easy to control my intake of food but at that time I usually give up and surrender to what are uncontrollable cravings for sweet things.' Katharina Dalton, in her book *Once a Month*, cites a study that took place in Canada among three hundred nurses which showed that there was a pronounced craving for carbohydrates and sweets and a desire to eat compulsively during the pre-menstrual time. The researchers suggested that this was the body's way of defending itself against a too severe or prolonged drop in blood sugar levels.

Women compulsive eaters find this an enormously

difficult time to cope with. The natural change in hormone levels alters the sugar tolerance and raises the level of the lower baseline so that the blood sugar level has not so far to drop before the 'emergency service' swings into action to provide the body with energy from glucose stores. This mobilization of the adrenals makes it easier to understand those sensations of panic, irritability, shiveriness, faintness or palpitations that attack a lot of women at the pre-menstrual time. Their bodies will not allow the blood sugar to fall below this baseline but when the glucose is drawn from cells to prevent this, they fill up with water, hence another familiar pre-menstrual symptom: water retention with its feeling of bloatedness and weight gain. The adrenals, as we have seen, release glucose from store which brings the hormone insulin into play. Stomach secretions become overactive which means that calcium is not absorbed. When there is a reduced blood calcium level this makes for irritability in the nervous system, causing muscle cramp and spasm.

How do we begin to break this vicious circle which strikes at women? Low blood sugar levels can be helped by obeying a few simple rules. Avoid caffeine, nicotine and alcohol and eat small but frequent meals that are balanced with nutrients in the correct combination; concentrate on fresh wholefoods; and shun those which are refined or processed. It may well be that the adrenal glands are exhausted because of the constant stress which has been put upon them. This condition results in an under-supply of calcium, the natural tranquillizer, which in conjunction with magnesium can be such a help in combating stress. If you are bulimic it is possible that your body may have too little potassium. Peter Hudson urges that these mineral requirements should be obtained in an organic form, such as kelp tablets or dolomite (natural magnesium-rich limestone), which are obtainable from health shops. If you habitually eat an unbalanced diet, it is likely you are lacking in some or all of the vitamin B group. This does not mean you should take massive doses of isolated vitamins but, if anything, a vitamin B complex.

On the subject of food supplements, there has been some controversy about our need for additional vitamins and minerals. While we would never suggest them as a substitute for an adequate, wholefood diet, it seems to be true that some people, compulsive eaters among them, may need more vitamins than others – vitamins and minerals that are not, for various reasons, obtained in their daily diet. We have seen a marked reduction in sugar craving when sufferers had made sure of an adequate supply of all the B vitamins. Your low blood sugar level that has given you all those unpleasant symptoms, including the desire to eat and eat and eat, may been have triggered off because you were particularly sensitive to a faulty diet. Your body then 'learned' that refined carbohydrate gave you a quick 'high' and you felt you could not do without 'something sweet' at regular intervals.

We know that escaping the vicious circle is not simply a question of rushing out to buy the right foods and preparing them carefully. The reason why you hesitate may be because you feel you 'need' those foods that are bad for you and you cannot see how you can change the habits of a lifetime. 'But I've always eaten it' is a too familiar phrase to our ears. We know the answer to our question: 'What do you truly want: a happy, healthy body or the taste of certain foods in your mouth for a few seconds?' When you develop a food sense you have what you want. Adequate nutrition, based on a fresh, wholefood diet, can help you think clearly and positively, give you zest and energy, confidence to finish whatever you began, and can firm up your body and make you look younger, longer. It can become such a habit to 'eat well' that you actually forget about food because your body is working so perfectly. Your weight normalizes without effort and your nerves relax so that you fall asleep the moment your head touches the pillow.

There is a tremendous difference between not being ill and experiencing radiant good health. Learn to recognize it. Think of the investment value of a sensible eating plan: all that you can put into life and all that you will get out of it. When your nutrition is wise and adequate, food becomes an ally not an enemy and eating is a daily delight. When your body and mind are united you will be able to step down from that destructive carousel and become one of *them*, and no longer one of *us*.

4 Ways Out

The work of the Maisner Centre

Many compulsive eaters who come to the Centre are desperate. Some have attempted suicide. Yet they represent merely the tip of the iceberg. Compulsive eating affects an enormous number of people, especially women. It is estimated that as many as one in ten people may be affected. The Maisner Method incorporates a mixture of relaxation therapy to combat stress and tension, guidance on nutrition and special dietary needs, with the aim of re-balancing the biochemical system, and lends a sympathetic ear, which does not condemn.

We stress that any attempt at control must begin by admitting that you have an eating problem. You must accept yourself as you are today and take responsibility for that self and its problems. Interviews with compulsive eaters at the Centre reveal that there are many who have had happy, secure childhoods but who have still become victims of an eating disorder. Sometimes, however, there are those who are so trapped by their past that they need full psychotherapy. In such cases, we admit our limitations and refer them on. They are people like Belinda who is currently working on her guilty, remorseful emotions with a trained therapist, while working simultaneously with us on other aspects of her eating problem.

No one is ever told to pull herself together nor given a conventional diet sheet. They are told they can learn to re-formulate their attitudes to food and come to accept it as a normal part of living. By doing so, they will regain their self-confidence and achieve control of themselves and their lives. The Centre aims at breaking the vicious circle of stress/food cravings/guilt/stress/food cravings and controlling the binge and starve pattern. While the approach is relaxed, compulsive eaters are expected to co-operate by filling in detailed questionnaires and later keeping a daily food chart. Their attitude will make a lot of difference to their success in achieving control. There are those who demand, 'What are you going to do for me?' and those who arrive with 'I'm happy that you can help me and I want to do everything in my power to help myself.' Success often depends on how much the sufferer is prepared to put into solving her problem.

The questionnaires require complete honesty on the part of the compulsive eater and complete confidentiality. They are comprehensive and include questions on personal life, family background, attitudes of relatives to the sufferer's problem, self-analysis of temperament and weaknesses, purpose in life and attitudes to the world in general. A second paper deals with the medical history, concentrating on weight problems, past therapies, stress habits, tranquillizers, appetite suppressants, laxatives and other addictive drugs. We discourage the use of all slimming tablets and feel that you should take diuretics only if they have been prescribed for a medical condition. When you take them arbitrarily, over a length of time, you deprive your body of important minerals that help in fat loss. We also suggest that you break yourself of the habit of taking laxatives, by halving the dose and then weaning yourself off them altogether. People on restricted diets often have problems with constipation so they are introduced to fibre and bran. Everyone knows the importance of unbroken sleep, particularly the night eater, but sleeping pills are worse than useless. You are encouraged to cut them down or ask your doctor for something weaker until you can wean yourself off them. And we suggest you try dolomite, which is rich in magnesium and calcium – nature's own calmant.

Within the questionnaires, there is a section on eating

when we try to pinpoint, with your co-operation, why you feel you have this disorder, when you binge, why you binge and the feelings centred around that binge. The evaluation of the questionnaires and subsequent food charts provide a number of clues to the problem. Malnutrition is notable among many compulsive eaters, so one of the initial steps is to try to persuade sufferers to adopt a balanced diet, and take an interest in good nutrition by having small, frequent meals throughout the day.

Also recommended are megadoses of the B vitamins and, if you smoke, vitamin C. This plan was suggested to Katherine whose health deteriorated when she left home to go to college. She became a bed-sitter binger because she had turned her back on her mother's wise eating plan. Many teenagers do this; it is part of the natural rebellion of adolescence. Katherine lived on cream buns and TV snacks. She was also under academic pressure as she was studying for exams. Her social life meant late nights and alcohol. Her metabolic system could take no more. Severe stress, and Katherine was subjected to several varieties all at once, increased her need for all nutrients. She also found that small, regular, well-balanced meals helped her to combat night eating and those nocturnal 'panics' of which she had complained.

Heather is a nursing sister who should have known better about her personal well-being. When sugar was suspected to be the culprit and she was advised to cut out all sugary, refined carbohydrate items from her diet, she protested. Later, Heather discovered that she suffered from chemical low blood sugar levels and was craving 'something sweet'. Her attitude changed completely when she adopted a diet high in protein and free from refined carbohydrates.

The food charts will also show up any potential or existing intolerance to food. Sometimes the pattern is remarkably clear. Take muesli, an intolerance to which we pick up time and again. The addict goes through a week in which muesli figures several times. And then she binges. When she cut it out, she began to find control. Take one of the writers' undoubted intolerance to dried fruit which she has learnt to avoid like the plague because she knows the chaos that will follow. Any diet that concentrates on a few isolated items is out as far as compulsive eaters are concerned, as is any food that figures constantly in binges.

This is a complicated story where nothing is exactly what it seems. Sometimes it appears to us like one of those sets of Chinese boxes where you open one only to reveal another. Sarah was doing well on a balanced eating plan until it came to Sunday lunch. She resented cutting out some of the food items and wrote on her chart: 'After that I could not stick to the diet and felt depressed and deprived for the rest of the week.' Now if a week's happiness depends on certain items in a Sunday lunch we felt she had some investigating to do. Sarah had always associated food with happiness, sought comfort in eating and had become stuck in that groove. Compulsive eaters have to find a way to stop non-productive thoughts, quieten the restlessness of their minds and conserve energy for positive action. Active meditation such as that encouraged by the Centre's deep relaxation tapes induces a state of mind receptive to new attitudes towards food and eating. Some people feel dubious when confronted by the idea of a form of hypnotherapy but it can be helpful with such problems. In that altered state of consciousness the system can more readily receive suggestions to adjust eating behaviour. The tapes also encourage deep breathing to help you to be more aware of your body so that you are better able to monitor the tension and relaxation of your muscles. People often find that they sleep better.

Relaxation is important but it is not the whole story. At times you need to galvanize yourself into action. You can go for months without bingeing but when you are bored you stuff yourself. We urge compulsive eaters to turn their backs on sabotage, and admit that at times there are probably certain foods you cannot keep in the house. What do we mean by sabotage? There was Veronica who bought a box of chocolates weeks and weeks before Christmas as a 'present' for a friend and then devoured the lot on a rainy, depressing evening when she felt at a loose end. There was Una who had the over-confidence to enrol for cake-decorating classes and proudly announced to us that she intended to give all the cakes to friends. She did so at first, but the inevitable occasion arrived when she felt bored and ate one herself and this led to a full-scale binge. You are controlled, not cured, we impress upon everybody with an eating disorder. It is an important piece of knowledge and you should always remember it and never sabotage that control.

Another part of the therapy is to set each compulsive eater a series of activities she must carry out within a week or a month. These involve changing habits, such as the time of taking a bath, wearing your hair in a different way, reading a book on an interesting subject or buying a series of 'treats' that have nothing to do with food. The aim is to change thinking patterns and to make them positive instead of negative. You are set reasonable goals, well within your scope, and the sense of achievement experienced makes you increasingly surprised at what you *are* capable of doing. Activities may be as simple as taking an unaccustomed walk, learning to notice things around you or making something on which you have to concentrate, but they help to revert ingrained, negative thought patterns.

Another activity on the list is to go out and pay someone a compliment every day. People are startled at how the world seems to be transformed. During her work with the hypnotherapist, Paulette remembers arriving at his office one morning and declaring: 'I don't know what's come over people – Mrs James smiled at me, and she is usually horrible, and also the bus conductor, and the milkman, too.' He laughed: 'It's not the world that has changed. It's you who have!'

Out of the cage: therapies and control

The story of you, the compulsive eater, who you are, what you do, and why you do it has much in common with a tale of detection. There are the clues, the red herrings, the painstaking unravelling and those moments of sudden insight. But perhaps most baffling of all is to find the solution. *Be patient*. It takes time! You did not become a compulsive eater overnight. It crept up on you. Whether the cause was environmental, social, psychological or physical, it came about because of the gradual wearing down of your body's defences through strain and pressures. So there is no instant 'cure', no magic wand to be waved, which will open the door of the cage. Slowly, however, you can uncoil that vicious circle, take control of your body and mind once more – and be free.

Life itself will not slow down or become more simple nor is it possible for you to opt out of all its responsibilities and expectations. But with a little wisdom, you can learn to choose a level of stress acceptable to you and to control how you body will react to it. You can reach the point of being able to tell yourself that everything is 'all right'. It is a great feeling to be in harmony with yourself, with the world around you and, what is probably most important to you, in control of what you eat. Your first step is to admit to yourself and to someone else that you have an eating disorder. You must overcome the idea that you are a failure.

You had been taught that it was wrong to express emotion and so you bottled it all up. The grief, fear and anger were repressed and this led to tension, frustration, a feeling of alienation and self-hatred. It destroyed relationships in your private life and at work, and you 'exploded' in wild bouts of eating. When you take this first positive step of getting it off your chest you release some of that tension, you begin to think more clearly, to see the situation more logically, and start acting more realistically. Usually it is easier to confide in a peer or someone who has 'been there' rather than in a doctor to whom you may feel you have to put on a brave face. There he is seated behind his desk looking wise and authoritative. How can you begin to describe your shameful habits? You invent a headache rather than explain what has suddenly become inexplicable. But you do need someone you feel you can trust, someone who will keep the secret between the two of you. That person might be a close friend or relative, a colleague, a fellow compulsive eater, or you might find you can become your own confidante by sitting down with pen and paper and writing out honestly the extent of your problem.

You might seek the help of a trained counsellor. There are many organizations which exist to help people who are distressed rather than disturbed. Counselling is becoming increasingly popular. Whereas, in the past, people in difficulty might go to a clinical psychologist or psychiatrist, now they can talk through their problem with a counsellor or therapist and without the trauma sometimes experienced when consulting a doctor. Even if they have not gone through an identical experience themselves, you can be sure that all such counsellors have had some deep, personal crisis in their own lives. They will be able to identify with you and they have that very important ability to listen while you talk. These may sound like natural gifts but in fact they are developed skills. Counselling has certain necessary limits. It does not offer advice or friendship but a chance to talk things through and to encourage you to realize your full potential. *You* are responsible and capable of making the necessary changes in your life although your counsellor can help you to see what options are available. He or she will also be much more effective if not over-involved in your problem.

Whether you choose to confide in a friend or relative, or talk to a counsellor, appointments and meeting places are a good idea. When you set a time and go to a quiet room where there is someone who understands you and is ready to listen, the right atmosphere is created to tackle the vicious circle.

Stress and metabolism are its cornerstones. We all have a glandular system regulated by a nervous system and both affect our metabolic pattern. The timing and intensity of daily changes in this activity are different for each of us. We all have our own system of gears, which accounts for everyone's differing needs of food and rest, output of energy, feelings of zest or fatigue and tolerance or intolerance to certain foods. Stress is the rate of wear and tear on the body and stressors are those activities or emotions which produce the wear and tear. But there are two kinds of stress: eustress, the healthy stress that gives a spice to life; and distress, the negative form that has to be controlled. The latter is brought about by destructive negative emotions and continuous mental or physical strain. What they have in common is that they activate your body's stress mechanism.

Your system can take a certain amount of stress and not all of it is harmful. We can all understand that heady feeling that helps us achieve an important goal when we say 'I can feel the adrenalin flowing!' But if it continued all the time we would be physically and emotionally drained. Your body learns to adapt to stress until it becomes exhausted because your particular metabolic pattern can no longer cope. If you ignore your body's 'early warning' signals, disorders like compulsive eating develop. According to one leading physician, we should cultivate a healthy respect for this feeling of fatigue, of 'I just cannot cope any longer!'

Physical and mental fatigue can make such inroads on your perspective and balance that you lose control. Compulsive eaters do not understand their metabolic patterns, nor do they understand the stress factors in their environment. They must re-educate themselves. They must understand their limitations and learn how to live within them.

With the help of your confidante, counsellor or you, yourself, you can begin to identify those things in your life that are causing you distress and manifesting themselves in an eating disorder. Throughout this book we have looked at a number of possible stressors. Some years ago, two American doctors, Thomas Holmes and Richard Rahe, drew up a table of what they called life change units and awarded a score to a variety of events. The higher the total, the more likely we are to suffer from a problem. The list is reproduced below. You may like to examine it and apply it to your own life style.

Events	*Life change unit*
Death of a spouse	100
Marital separation	65
Death of close family member	63
Personal injury or illness	53
Marriage	50
Loss of job	47
Marital reconciliation	45
Retirement	45
Change in health of family member	44
Wife's pregnancy	40
Sex difficulties	39
Gain of a new family member	39
Change in financial status	38
Death of a close friend	37
Change to a different kind of work	36
Increase or decrease in arguments with spouse	35
Taking out a large home mortgage	31
Foreclosure of mortgage or loan	30
Change in work responsibilities	29
Son or daughter leaving home	29
Trouble with in-laws	29
Outstanding personal achievement	28
Wife beginning or stopping work	26
Revision of personal habits	24
Trouble with business superior	23
Change of working hours or conditions	20
Change in residence	20
Change in schools	20
Change in recreation	19

Events	*Life change unit*
Change in social activities	18
Taking out a small home mortgage	17
Change in sleeping habits	16
Change in number of family get-togethers	15
Change in eating habits	15
Vacation	13
Minor violation of law	11

In order to arrive at your personal score you should go through the list and tick the life changes that have affected you within the last year. As a guide to deciding the level of risk you run: if you score over 300 life change units your stress level is too high; between 200 and 300, your risk is medium. If you have between 150 and 200 life change units scored then your stress level is probably within a safe limit.

Dr Vernon Coleman, in his book *Stress Control*, cited factors such as environmental pressures, big city life, changes in family life, television, women's emancipation and the 'housewife's syndrome' as potential stressors. He described the modern housewife surrounded by kitchen machines that give her more freedom but much less satisfaction, and who is bored and frustrated by the apparent insignificance of her role. This must be familiar to many a compulsive eater. Discovering the likely causes of stress in your life is very important. When you have made an honest attempt to track them down, voice them and write them down. You can then begin to evaluate them. You certainly won't be able to avoid all stress. Some is pleasant, some necessary – life would be dull without it – but some is avoidable. Weighing it all up, and deciding whether there are more positive or more negative aspects to the stress-inducing activities in your life, develops your sense of control. *You* are in command, *you* can accept or reject the pressures and understand how many you can take without life becoming intolerable.

You may think you know yourself well, but when you make a sustained effort to discover who you are and what is going on around you, you may be in for some surprises. You may discover that things you imagined you liked are not as precious as you once thought. On the other hand, you may find that some of those things you thought you disliked are not as awful as they seemed. You can practise yoga, you can thrash it out with your counsellor or confidante or you can revert to pen and paper. Whichever method you choose, knowing yourself is crucial to the understanding of how these strains and pressures affect you as an individual, and it will give you the self-assurance to deal with them. Learn to recognize your priorities both in your private and work life. Every one of us has goals. What are yours? Do you want to make a fortune? Beat the Joneses at their own game? Enjoy better love-making? Travel? For goodness sake, be honest! Bring it all out! Do not be afraid of admitting your ambition to yourself and to others, whatever it is. Left unspoken it may set up conflicts that your mind will deal with in its own, possibly destructive, way.

Perhaps these goals are too unrealistic? Perhaps they are not ambitious enough? Are you neglecting areas of your life? Do you never buckle down to the task in hand? Take a long look at your habits. Make a list and decide which ones are worth holding on to and which you will eliminate. Gradually, you can learn to view things and people clearly and honestly and, most difficult of all, see yourself as you are. Perhaps you will find this easier to come to terms with when you realize that we had this ability once before as babies. Children see the world as it really is and they are relaxed and serene within themselves. Your first aim should be to become intensely aware of your position in life, as a child is aware, and then become conscious of the body you wish to shape and control. You have the ability to change almost anything you wish to, but first you must know what it is you want to change and be sure that the goal you set yourself is the best one for you.

Real self-knowledge, however you gain it, can give you a

new peace of mind and spirit and can allow you to stand back and see your compulsive eating for what it is. If you find yourself unavoidably in what you have always thought of as an 'unpleasant' situation, learn to face it, experience it and overcome it. The moment you stop being fearful, you automatically release yourself from tensions and anxieties. You have also released that energy which was tied up with resistance. It means thay you face the bogey men as they appear and never allow the fear of them to prevent you from feeling and experiencing. If you can become at one with your surroundings, you are less vulnerable to the anxieties and sufferings, which make daily life fraught with apprehension and turn you towards the tranquilliser of food. A technique like this can help compulsive eaters attune themselves to their bodies.

If you stop fearing food and allow yourself to trust your body you can begin to explore your abnormal use of food. This kind of self-knowledge can help to release you, calm you – not by being 'drugged' with food but by making you realize that control comes from attending to other needs you may have. When you are at one with your own body you can begin to understand the outside pressures that are reinforcing these distorted attitudes to food. Compulsive eaters are always bemoaning the fact that their behaviour is not normal and they make this a barrier between the ranks of *us* and *them*. Being so-called 'normal' depends to a great extent on where you are, whom you are with and what you are doing. Part of the solution is to move among human beings who make you feel fulfilled, do something about your boredom, make the most of what you are, and try to understand and truly be that self. Lack of fulfilment makes us less able to cope with strains from the world outside. The more we feel at one with our environment, the less we are likely to suffer from stress and its effects upon us. If there is a balance of give and take between you and your family or friends, you have a good 'prop' system. If your job is interesting, you will have a sense of work satisfaction. Every kind of work has its boring moments, some more than others. If you feel yours does not demand enough of you, use your leisure time to stretch your capabilities further by finding hobbies or new interests.

Try not to let yourself become buried in a welter of trivia but learn how to select those things that are important to you and forget those that are less so. Sit down with your pen and paper and, again, write down your thoughts. Work out your basic aims in life, set some goals for both personal and public life and refer to these frequently to check how far you are nearing their achievement and revise them if necessary. Take a closer look at your day-to-day routine and see whether you are in the habit of rushing through too many tasks in twenty-four hours. By allowing yourself more time to meet deadlines you can give yourself opportunities to enjoy leisure pursuits, which, in turn, make you feel more in control of your situation. Try rising earlier in the morning and give yourself time for a stroll or simply sit and think in peace. See that your surroundings are orderly and pleasing to the eye. Allow other people to voice their views and try to concentrate on what they are saying instead of always trying to press *your* point. What you are doing is conducting a 'normalizing' process which you can control with your own mind. The more you believe in the image of the person you wish to be, and the shape you feel is true for you, the nearer you come to achieving it.

While you are re-educating your body and mind, you should be kind to yourself and try to ensure that the emotional side of you is as quiet and calm as possible. If they are avoidable, banish the jobs that you know are likely to upset your feeling of harmony. Shun events that you know from experience are emotionally draining. If you know there are people who bring out your negative, hostile feelings, avoid them, and choose the company of those who make you feel positive and elevated. There are 'trigger people' as well as 'trigger foods' and you are not being cowardly in protecting yourself while you learn to gain control. If you have to face such situations, try to keep the atmosphere light and humorous. Be self-assertive, not aggressive. Learn to say 'no'.

You are looking at familiar surroundings and situations with a fresh eye and learning to make friends with them. But where are *you* in this scheme of things and who are you? Forget self-consciousness and try the following exercise: say out loud who you are and where you are. If this makes you feel silly it is an indication that you are being cheated out of being yourself. Lack of identity or a very blurred sense of personal wants and needs is characteristic of many compulsive eaters. Take the housewife who is angry and resentful about the unreasonable demands made on her by her family. She suppresses these feelings because she feels she 'ought not to feel that way'. The stress continues, wears her down, and she binges.

There are many irrational beliefs about self-assertiveness. Women, in particular, feel that it is rude and selfish to say what they want or need. Anyway, they think those people who are close to them should know how they feel without their having to communicate it. There is the suggestion that a woman loses her femininity if she asserts herself. You should learn to brush aside those anxieties and doubts about how people will respond to your requests. Instead of fretting and working yourself up over the roundabout and difficult ways you might use to get someone to do something for you, ask them. It is simple: just ask. Immediately, your feeling of frustration will lift. If you hum and haw and beat about the bush it is likely you will only annoy other people. Assertive behaviour can actually strengthen communication. It is when you are reticent or 'foggy' about your needs and wants, that a relationship can falter. If it helps, write down exactly what you need or want and then try to express it as specifically as possible. Remember, there should be a valid reason behind any request and you should take just one need at a time so that it is not confused with other issues. Never use an apologetic, 'I'm sorry' phrase, but something like 'I need . . .', or 'I want . . .'. Instead of muttering, 'I say, what would you think of . . .', say 'I'd like to . . .'. Discuss the subject of requests with family or friends. Find out their views. There is much too much blurredness-about-the-edges in our requests of one another. They are responsible for a lot of misunderstandings. Anticipate that you will receive a positive response from the people of whom you ask for something. If your approach is filled with indifference, resentment or downright dislike then you will deserve a cool reception to any request you make. The natural laws of cause and effect come into play. If you approach people with consideration, friendship and optimism, you will arouse a similar response in them.

Once again, please be patient because your rigid attitudes will take time to bend. More than likely, the change will come about as the result of a series of small alterations in your behaviour rather than as an overnight dramatic change. But, ask! Use 'please' and 'thank you' to oil the wheels and never command or give an order. Your sense of being in control of these needs and giving yourself permission to voice them can be reflected in a more controlled way of eating. If you choose to be positive instead of negative, you can tune into these natural laws and make them work for you.

You have the right to make a request and you also have the right to refuse it. There is an art in saying 'no' and meaning it. Many compulsive eaters are convinced that the wants and needs of other people should come before their own and that other people cannot cope with a refusal. As a result, they often agree to unwelcome requests which have a bad effect on their emotions. They feel helpless, isolated and unable to communicate their true feelings to the other person – and so they binge. They find themselves spending far too much time on things that are unpleasant to them and have little time for their own priorities so that they end up feeling exploited, lose self-respect, and binge. You can learn to say 'no' and continue to say it, even when confused by a very aggressive or manipulative person. This involves making it clear that the other person has been heard and the situation understood but that it is not possible for the request to be carried out. 'Yes, I know you will not be able to go out tonight if there is no one to babysit for you. I am sorry but on this occasion I cannot do it for you.' 'Yes, I understand that you were held up in a traffic-jam but it is now too late for you to start decorating the kitchen because I want to go out.' It is surprising how very difficult this positive approach is to many compulsive eaters but it is essential that they learn to refuse when it is in their best interests to do so.

Start saying 'yes' to all and sundry, to each and every request, however unreasonable, and you are apt to continue to say 'yes', uncontrollably, then despise yourself and binge. Learn when to say 'no' and, gradually, you can gain the self-perception which will help you to overcome the urge to eat. Remember, if you do not like what is happening to you today and have had the courage to admit it to yourself, imagine how much worse the situation would be in ten years' time and how much further you would have been sucked into that vacuum of self-pity, self-hatred and bingeing. Begin today: assert yourself and discover the ability to say 'no'.

Your body has come under siege from the strains and pressures that surround it. If you make a real effort to build up and maintain your body in an optimum state of health it can better defend itself. When your diet is adequate and balanced, your weight normalizes. When you exercise regularly, your body becomes toned up, controlled, and all this helps you to deal better with any assault from your immediate environment. No one needs this defence more urgently than the compulsive eaters and yet there seems to be quite a serious level of malnutrition among them. Sugary, refined carbohydrates, 'empty' calories appear continually in their diets, often coupled with a refusal to eat good wholefoods in the mistaken belief they are 'fattening'. Some binge simply because they are hungry or because their bodies crave the components of good fresh food, which they are not receiving. The system understands these needs, sends up demands and the response comes back in the form of chocolate bars and packets of crisps. Gradually, the demands become distorted and eating becomes wild and indiscriminate. There is no magic about the efficient production of energy. You will experience those unpleasant symptoms of fatigue and negative mood changes if you do not sustain a good standard of nutrition, for you can only use up the energy you generate.

Peter Hudson stresses the need for resoluteness and intelligence in dietary matters: 'for it requires no small effort of one's will to forsake the old, incorrect and suicidal dietetic traditions and intelligently and persistently put into practice natural principles of nutrition and sane living.' People are not laboratory animals that are fed a diet with a deficiency in just one nutrient. They may be suffering from several deficiencies and their symptoms are vague, uncomfortable and accumulative and, in the case of the compulsive eater, they end in a binge. Because of irregular eating habits, blood sugar levels may be low at some times of the day, which can account for moodiness, tension, depression and gorging. The first rule for a good nutrition programme is that it must be balanced to supply as many of the body's requirements as possible and be suitable to your way of life. Changes should be gradual. You cannot do it all overnight. But as your mind and body become more balanced, you will also find your eating habits become so, too, and vice versa. This is a positive turn in the vicious circle.

It is interesting to look at those people in whom the body/mind balance is well achieved. Practitioners of yoga, for example, often adopt what is known as a lacto-vegetarian diet. This is a diet that possesses the characteristics which modern nutritionists are recommending to all. And it is no coincidence. Early in the century, Dr Robert McCarrison, a pioneer in nutrition, noted that the Hunza tribe followed a diet which was so perfect that their only illnesses were climbing accidents. His experiments also revealed that refined and processed food diets, familiar to many compulsive eaters, were nutritionally as bad as the worst he had found in India. The rules he established go hand in hand with modern-day thinking and are almost identical to those handed down by yogis over the years. A cardinal rule is that all food must be fresh and grains should be freshly milled and left whole to make brown bread, flour and rice. Food should be cooked for the minimum time and fresh fruit and vegetables should form a large part of any diet. Meat and fish are optional, provided there is a good supply of protein coming from other sources, such as milk products or the soya bean. Vitamins and minerals should also be adequately supplied.

Peter Hudson, in the course of his homeopathic practice, has found that such diets high in vegetables, fruits and natural, unrefined carbohydrates are useful in weight reduction because they provide additional bulk in a lower calorie diet and are therefore more filling and less stimulating. 'I find that some obese individuals prefer them to a conventional meat-containing, low calorie diet,' he writes. These complex, natural carbohydrates have nothing in common with their poor relations, the processed, refined, often chemical-ridden carbohydrates, which are apt to spark off binges. They contain essential minerals and vitamins, such as magnesium and vitamin B6, which are vital for good metabolism and balance of the system. A diet high in these can be balanced quite easily by the addition of sufficient protein and fats, not neglecting the so-called 'second-class' plant proteins, which, recent research has shown, can be combined so that the resultant mixture has a higher nutritional value than individual, first-class proteins. And common sense makes a better seasoner than salt!

Compulsive eaters know they should eat less. But if they eat less they feel deprived. Small meals do not provide the familiar over-full stomach, while a diet without sugar will not give that 'lift' they have come to rely on. They will probably find that when they experiment with fresh wholefoods, they are very satisfying. Vegetable soups are filling, not fattening; and a baked jacket potato or whole brown rice is more filling than their devitalized counterparts. There is no need to fear such carbohydrates nor banish them from the diet altogether. If you have become accustomed to stuffing yourself with quantities of these refined foods, you will be surprised how much better you begin to feel, and how much more energy you have on a good wholefood eating plan.

But food sense is not simply a matter of knowing what is 'good' for you, buying it, preparing it with care and eating it. A great deal has to do with changing your attitude from negative to positive. 'But I can't afford it' is no excuse. Thousands of people are living on items that are not worth carrying home from the supermarket, let alone eating. These non-foods crowd out proteins, unrefined, complex carbohydrates, fats, vitamins and minerals.

'Why should I give up what I enjoy?' or, 'how boring having to plan what I eat' are other characteristic remarks of the compulsive eater who is reluctant to make a change. Once you have established a balanced eating plan that is right for you – one that cuts out any 'trigger foods' and ensures that you take a sufficient quantity of health-giving items – you will not need to spend much time thinking about it. No longer will it be a boring end in itself, an over-faddy attitude and, often, painful experience, but it will become a goal to health, both physical and mental, and to emotional stability, which will help you to control your eating and allow you to enjoy life to the full.

Body and mind are so inextricably tied together that if you are snarling up the metabolic traffic within your system, your thoughts will be pessimistic and self-centred, which is no passport to good relations with those around you.

Become aware of sugar: examine the label on every packet or tin of your 'favourite' supermarket foods and you will be startled to discover exactly what it is you are eating and how frequently sugar appears, even in those foods you would never connect with sweetness. Take control of how sugar enters your body. Do not allow this insidious undermining of your eating behaviour.

Compulsive eaters will protest, initially, when asked to cut out sugar from their diets, but their attitude changes completely when they adopt a wholefood diet, free of refined, processed foods, and one where mini-meals are eaten more frequently. Such an eating plan offers a slow release of blood sugar throughout the day and keeps your mood more even, with none of the dangerous 'highs' and 'lows' that set you on the binge/fast roundabout. Very often, this cutting out of sugar and packeted items, which contain chemicals, will give you withdrawal symptoms but this is not because your new attitudes are wrong. The symptoms soon pass, leaving in their wake a sense of well-being, a zest for life and a relaxed body and mind.

Fad or crash diets exacerbate low blood sugar levels, food intolerance and metabolic imbalance, not to mention an increase in the feeling of psychological deprivation. They lead to malnutrition and multiple deficiencies that cause symptoms of varying discomfort where food, especially sugar and carbohydrates in the refined processed forms, is used as a tranquillizer. If you are an obese, compulsive eater, forget calorie counting and shun the bathroom scales. Concentrate on building up health and balance. When the quality of food is improved while the quantity in terms of 'empty' calories is reduced, blood sugar is kept to its optimum level and the craving for 'something sweet' disappears. Be patient. There will be no dramatic weight loss but on such a course you can normalize your weight and keep it stable for the rest of your life.

Variety is the keyword when any kind of hypersensitivity to food manifests itself. Whatever you eat, even your good wholefoods, make them as varied as your pocket and imagination allow. Nothing is 'healthy' when you begin to eat it to the exclusion of everything else until your body becomes intolerant to it. Moderation in all things could not hold more meaning than among those people who suspect extra-sensitivity to food. The usual treatment is elimination dieting which is hard to follow without the help of an allergy expert. In the event of your suspecting such hypersensitivity, you would do well to consult a specialist. But if you believe you know the 'trigger', the simplest advice is to cut it right out of your diet. If you wish to test yourself, try eating it again after a while and see whether the symptoms return or the binges begin again. Make an effort to see that foods are as whole and unadulterated as possible. Keep them simple: no packets, sauces or condiments of which the contents are unknown to you. Ring the changes. Experiment with the whole range of vegetables and fruit available to you. It is amazing how many people stick to the same old thing, day in and day out, never venturing beyond conventional cabbage or apples, or experimenting with the cuisine of other countries. At first, it might seem dull that you have to cut out so many of the items you 'like' but you also give yourself the chance to discover a whole new world of wonderful choices. A third piece of advice is that you should rotate your diet so that your body can have a rest before it has to deal with the same food again. The overall idea is not to deprive yourself but to develop a new attitude towards food. As one doctor wisely said: 'It is like putting money in the bank which will be a pleasure to spend.' In time, you will realize how good nutrition is vitally related to your balance and control.

Peter Hudson writes: 'The blood stream with its marvellous distribution system carries the essentials that provide the energy and vitality for the functioning of every part of the organism. How we will fare in twenty-four hours from now will depend upon the nature of the food we have taken into our stomachs, today.' Because you may be extra-sensitive to stress in all its forms, your requirements are higher than those people who react less and you might need nutritional supplements. These can never be a substitute for good wholesome food but if you are suffering from the effects of long-term, faulty eating they will give you nutrients in the quantity you need.

Physical fitness is essential as part of your strategy in

waging war against an eating disorder. When you exercise regularly, you are improving your system's condition to withstand physical and mental pressures. When your muscles, lungs and heart are strengthened through proper use, you will feel better and look better, be less anxious and aggressive and be able to cope better with problems. The best exercise for anyone wishing to improve her general health and strengthen herself against the strains of life will not be competitive. The moment you pit yourself against someone else, or strive to hold a place within a group, you are only adding to your pressures. As a compulsive eater, your aim is somewhat special: you want to improve the functioning of your heart and lungs so that your body's energy delivery system is more efficient, and create a more relaxed and capable individual, thus reducing the level of stress in your life. Endurance or aerobic exercise will be your best choice. The advantages are many: it will help your body to deliver oxygen to your whole system; it will aid your digestive functions and help you to relax and sleep better; and it will minimize the adverse effects of tension and stress.

Situations pressurize us and our bodies react by releasing the adrenalin – 'fight or flight' hormone – into our blood stream. There it stays, rather like a car caught up in a traffic jam while the driver's foot stays on the throttle. In our society we have little opportunity to express our emotions and are encouraged to repress our responses so that harmful consequences may result. Exercise helps to use up the hormone in a positive way. As your fitness improves so does your self-confidence and self-image. You become more self-aware and disciplined and in better control of your eating behaviour. Walking, jogging, running, swimming and dancing are all excellent ways of building up your anti-stress, pro-control system. But whatever type of exercise you choose, take things slowly, don't rush it. Be patient with yourself and don't expect immediate results.

According to Richard Hittleman, teacher and writer of yoga, the criterion for any regime undertaken in connection with weight reduction, regulation or diet control should be comfortable, even enjoyable, and denial, guilt and discipline should be reduced to a minimum. 'Control,' he says, 'implies a battle.' But there is another kind of control, which suggests co-ordination and balance. Yoga, which can be done anywhere, particularly in the privacy of your home without fear of failure, promotes this balance and can become a natural way of life. Yoga exercises have as their goal the promotion of a healthy, whole body and mind.

Whether you choose swimming, running or yoga, exercise helps to balance your body and regulate your heart beat, which, in turn, oxygenates your body. Stimulants, such as alcohol and cigarettes, activate the beat of your heart abnormally and upset the balance of the adrenal glands. Compulsive eaters often claim that they 'need' these props to help them cope with difficult situations or to communicate with others. They smoke and drink, hoping to relieve stress but if they can kick the habits, the resultant increase in fitness and confidence is more likely to reduce their overall reaction to pressures. Anyone seeking to control an eating disorder is strongly advised to stop drinking altogether and to stop smoking or at least cut down. If you feel you need help, anti-smoking clinics are on the increase and you do not have to be an alcoholic to join Alcoholics Anonymous. Think about all the positive advantages in giving up smoking and drinking. Avoid, at least initially, situations that you have always associated with those habits. Give yourself 'treats', paid for out of the money you have saved on smoking – a visit to the cinema, new clothes, a book or record. Get into the habit of saying: 'No, thank you, I don't smoke' and 'I don't drink.'

You are re-thinking your life style. You are remodelling your eating, exercising, and smoking and drinking habits. While you are involved in this you should teach yourself to relax at certain times of the day. There is nothing complicated or special about this. It is a pity that the words 'relaxation' and 'meditation' have become offputting to some people because they have been linked to money-making organizations and to mystical experiences. All the words represent is control techniques, ones that we can all learn with a little patience and practice and from which we can gain the physical and mental benefits they have to offer. Relaxation techniques, once perfected, give you a sense of serenity and well-being and help you to feel in control. Once learned, they will provide you with an excellent and lasting defence against the slings and arrows of life. We cannot escape them entirely, but we can control the effect these stressors have on us by discovering the secret of inner peace through relaxation.

There are several methods you might try to find out which is the most effective for you. Each of them has the same goal: to reduce stress and enable you to feel in control of yourself and your eating behaviour. At the beginning, while you are teaching yourself to relax, it is best to be in a quiet place where you are not likely to be disturbed; to concentrate on an object to which you can re-direct your mind if it begins to wander; to have a passive mental attitude in which you do not over-concentrate but allow those intruding thoughts to pass through your mind and out again; and to be in a comfortable position – probably sitting down rather than lying. Give yourself twenty minutes each day for a relaxation session. You will be surprised how progressively easy it becomes to let your body and mind 'go' at your command during these periods.

At first you will tell each part of your body to tense and then let go: feet, legs, trunk, chest, arms, neck, etc. Or you can try a mental approach by allowing all your muscles to feel heavy and then concentrating on the inhalation and exhalation of your breath, pronouncing 'one' every time you breathe out. Perhaps you will create your own private retreat. As you make your body heavy and relaxed, you 'send' your mind walking through this beautiful place where the leaves are green against a sunlit blue sky and there is the gentle sound of waves washing up on the shore. You feel the peace and quiet surrounding you and you mentally absorb it.

Initially, to anyone with an eating disorder, impulsive as well as compulsive, these suggestions may seem alien, almost impossible to carry out, but you can learn techniques to control your mind. Instead of relying on tranquillizers and sleeping tablets, which at best give you a short respite from exhaustion, you, yourself, can control the bombardment of stressors that attack your body and mind and learn to defuse them consistently. Your eating disorder has come about because of the way you live and the way in which your system has reacted to that life style. Learn to relax, control what flows through your mind and your eating behaviour will also change.

Inner calm provides a key to the cage. By healing splits in your personality and bringing your mind and body together into harmony, you are relaxed and freed from a perpetual state of fear, anxiety and insecurity. You realize that it is you who have imprisoned yourself in that cage with its thick bars and you have forgotten the freedom outside. As control comes you experience a sense of liberty and lightness.

Breathing is another way of controlling the body and mind and bringing them together. It is used as therapy by people like Harriet Karsh who has made compulsive eating one of her studies. As you inhale and draw air deep within you, you become aware of the very action of breathing and, by allowing the process full rein, you also allow yourself to experience feelings that have been stored away in the body.

A major sign of stress is short, shallow breathing, which is an attempt to dampen down the stress feelings. When you breathe more deeply, you allow more energy to be mobilized to deal with the situation. The level of emotion may rise initially but as you learn through deep and correct breathing to focus on the here and now, you can shed the negative emotions, usually a backwash from past experiences of grief, guilt, anger and fear, and accept the challenge of the stress and feel more capable of dealing with it. Yoga urges us not to be afraid of being alive. When we breathe correctly we acknowledge that all, not just parts, of our body is alive. We cannot be healthy or happy unless we allow this to happen.

The road to controlling your eating problem can begin today. With the help of the preceding suggestions you can take an honest look at your life style and change those parts of it you do not like, accepting those you cannot change and selecting your personal threshold of stress. You cannot eliminate the pressures completely but you need not put up with those that are not worth the effort. There may be some things you cannot eliminate but you can make use of 'little escapes' to ease them. These might take the form of a few days' holiday, even one day or a few hours, when you please yourself and nobody else. It could be a 'treat', a visit to the theatre, a present or making some improvement to your personal appearance. These little escapes will depend on your life style. If you are always rushing about, a restful time will be a contrast. If yours is a sedentary existence, an active hobby or sport could provide the necessary 'break'.

Establish a 'quiet place' – the yogis call it an 'ashram' – somewhere where you can go for a quiet hour, just to be yourself and where you will not be disturbed. If you truly wish it, there is always somewhere and some time where you can find peace and quiet for a 'little escape'. If you find life crowds in on you and threatens to take over, make lists and tick off each item as you complete it. It is surprising the sense of control this can give you. Your ability to cut off for a while and retreat into your 'ashram' sets up the process of balance and 'normalization' that you are creating. It should become a way of life. You are what you think and feel in the same way as you are what you eat.

Watch your face in the mirror when you smile. It is not easy to look happy and feel sad at the same time. You have in your power the ability to change. If you change just the muscles, it will only be a mask. Try to alter the expression in your eyes and almost without effort you'll change the attitude behind those eyes. Remember, you are what you think. Your mind can make you what you want to be.

Laughter is a wonderful physical and mental tonic. Dr Beren Wolfe, in his book *How to be Happy though Human*, points out that a sense of humour is valuable in making us more objective. If we can only detach ourselves to some extent from the way things affect us and see them as if they were on a comedy stage, we could laugh with ourselves and at ourselves. Laughter certainly plays an important role in that 'sound mind in a healthy body' adage.

In the end, it is your choice whether you stay in the cage or whether you decide to take action and free yourself. It is not what happens to you but what you make of life that really counts. Though the bars of the cage seem thick, you can be free. Cultivate your sense of humour. Be brave. Be human. Have the courage to be yourself.

Bibliography

John Archer and Barbara Lloyd, *Sex and Gender* (Pelican, 1982)

Robert Atkins, *Nutrition Breakthrough* (Bantam Books, 1982)

William Bennett and Joel Gurin, *The Dieter's Dilemma* (Basic Books, 1982)

Hilde Bruch, *The Golden Cage: Enigma of Anorexia Nervosa* (Open Books, 1978)

Martin Budd, *Low Blood Sugar (Hypoglycaemia): the Twentieth-century Epidemic?* (Thorsons, 1981)

Vernon Coleman, *Stress Control* (Pan Books, 1978)

Peter Dally and Joan Gomez, *Obesity and Anorexia Nervosa: a Question of Shape* (Faber and Faber, 1980)

Katharina Dalton, *Once a Month* (Fontana, 1978)

Adelle Davis, *Let's Eat Right to Keep Fit* (Allen and Unwin, 1971)

Pamela Dixon, *New Ways with Fresh Fruit and Vegetables* (Faber and Faber, 1981)

Hetty Einzig and Geoffrey Cannon, *Dieting Makes You Fat* (Century Publishing, 1983)

D. H. Fink, *Release from Nervous Tension* (Allen and Unwin, 1979)

Gayelord Hauser, *Look Younger, Live Longer* (Faber and Faber, 1960)

Ray Hill, 'The best thing since sliced bread' in *Healthy Living* (December 1983)

Marion Hilliard, *Women and Fatigue* (Pan Piper, 1963)

Thomas Holmes and Richard Rahe, 'The social readjustment rating scale' in *Journal of Psychosomatic Research* (Pergamon Press, 1967)

Peter J. Hudson, *Why Die Young?* (Pryor Publications, 1983)

Penelope Leach, *Baby and Child* (Michael Joseph, 1977)

Richard Mackarness, *Not All in the Mind* (Pan Books, 1976)

Jean Baker Miller, *Towards a New Psychology of Women* (Pelican, 1978)

Susie Orbach, *Fat is a Feminist Issue* (Hamlyn, 1979)

Vance Packard, *The Hidden Persuaders* (Pelican, 1962)

Theron G. Randolph and Ralph W. Moss, *Allergies: Your Hidden Enemy* (Turnstone Press, 1981)

Caroline Shreeve, *Pre-Menstrual Syndrome* (Thorsons, 1983)

L. M. Vincent, *Competing with the Sylph* (Andrews and McMeel, 1979)

Index